Brightening Over Dillon's

Liam Nevin

First Published in 2016 by The Manuscript Publisher

ISBN: 978-0-9576729-9-4

A CIP Catalogue record for this book is available from the National Library

Typesetting, page design and layout, cover design by DocumentsandManuscripts.com

Brightening Over Dillon's

Dedication

to Kate, Lynda and Dylan

Acknowledgements

My family; brothers, John, Joe, Seamus, Peter and Pat and sister, Ann, for sharing their experiences. My dear friend, Colm Nelson, for sharing his memories of events, many of which I had forgotten and Niamh Collins, archivist at Dalgan Park, who provided me with much insight into the lives of clerical students. I am grateful for books – such as *JFK in Ireland* by Ryan Tubridy and *Fat God, Thin God* by James Kennedy and an account of Father Willie Doyle by KV Turley – for information of the period and before and, I must confess, I borrowed a swear word from my favourite author, John McGahern.

Foreword

Growing up in the sixties wasn't always easy; the houses were often overcrowded with not many facilities such as running water and central heating. School could be quite difficult, with corporal punishment a major issue. It was believed by many teachers that education could be 'beaten' into pupils. But life was happy and there was little pressure on children to have this that and the other.

Most families hadn't much. There were no computers with all that that entails, no mobile phones and only limited television. Children made up their own games and played football and other sports all year around. They could play very safely outdoors and were free to explore the fields and woods and to invent adventures.

I have tried to paint a picture of that time and, with the help of family and friends, drawing on my own experiences and theirs too to do so. It is not intended as a wholly historical account of the period, or of any particular family of that time but I tried to include many actual events in Ireland, as they occurred.

Contents

Summer Holidays

Sean Noonan, aged eleven-and-a-half, sat on the old chair that his grandfather made, many years before, from an old tree trunk cut into in a half circle and a large piece of black thorn, bent to make both arms and the back. It had three legs, a large cushion and was painted black. He gazed out through the open door, towards the morning sunshine at the laurel hedge the other side of the narrow road. It was early July 1961 and it was the first day of the long summer holidays that would last up to the beginning of September – nearly two whole months.

He was so relieved that the holidays had come at last. It had been a tough year at school. His last teacher at the boys' national school, Mister O'Keefe, was tough. He took no nonsense and dished out the slaps, with his carefully prepared stick, without hesitation. When a stick had come to be of no further use, a boy was selected to go to one of the nearest hedges and bring back a suitable replacement. Often, the 'specimen' brought back was rejected, being too weak or too thick and the boy would be sent out again. A few months back, it had been Sean's turn; the 'specimen' was accepted. Mister O'Keefe would then spend some time crafting it with a penknife into a suitable instrument of torture. His other favourite 'torture' for the class was to pull hard on a boy's ear, having approached from behind and then whack him on the side of the head saying, "turn up, you goat", the meaning of which eluded Sean and his classmates.

The boys' national school consisted of three rooms. It was the standard layout of the Irish village school built in the nineteen-forties, with three tall windows to each classroom. The window ledge was quite high up, so the students could not see directly out:

they could only see the sky and the tops of taller trees. Each room had a solid fuel burner. The boys were required to bring in money to pay for turf or coal. Before Sean's time the pupils had to bring in the fuel – a few sods of turf or some coal – themselves. In cold winter days, the teacher often hogged the stove, letting out little heat to the shivering boys seated in their wood and iron two-seater desks. The school had an inside toilet, a small staff room for the teachers and a concrete play-yard with a long open shelter along one side. There was also an open grassed area enclosed by hedges to play in. The school was situated less than half a mile from the village itself. Between the village and the school were the church (chapel) and the parish priest's house.

Sean lived with his parents, his two sisters and four of five brothers in a small, two-bedroomed cottage with one kitchen/living room. Outside, at the back of the house, there stood a concrete building containing a 'dry' toilet and a pig house. There was a large garden, divided by a six-foot hedge; on one side, there was a fruit and vegetable area with a lawn and the on the other side, there was a 'haggart', which consisted of various cow or storage sheds, a 'tool' shed and an area where the hayrick was erected at harvest time. Inside the kitchen/dining/living room, there was a settle-bed, a large 'farmhouse' wooden table, two fireside chairs, a dresser and a sideboard. The settle-bed was, in fact, a wooden settee, which opened downwards to make a double bed. The bed was simply a mattress on wood, which could be quite uncomfortable. Two of Sean's older brothers slept here.

The open fire had a brick surround and a black hob on each side. An iron plate could be swung from the hob to the fire. There was an iron pole over the fire on which the kettle hung but there was no running water. Water was carried by bucket from the pump about fifty yards up the road. The kitchen had several pictures hung on the walls. Most were religious. There was the Sacred Heart, which hung over the mantelpiece, together with a red lamp, which was permanently lit. Over the settle-bed hung a picture of Pope Pius XI and a picture featuring a Venetian scene – not religious, if St. Mark's Church is not counted. The bedrooms also had religious pictures adorning the walls. There was one of Christ the King, with shafts of light proceeding from His hands, lighting up the earth. When Sean saw shafts of light coming from the clouds, he would be reminded of this picture.

The bedrooms were cluttered with furniture, ranging from beds, of course, to side-tables and chests of drawers and a wardrobe. Each of the bedrooms had a small open fire but these were seldom used. Father's bedroom had a wash stand over which hung a large mirror. On the stand was a ceramic white basin and water jug. Underneath the stand was a chamber pot (or po) for emergency use only, no solids! Normally the boys were expected to relieve themselves outside. In fact, they used the local fields for all their toiletry requirements, especially in the summer months, using 'natural' toilet paper in the form of dock leaves.

The Noonan family lived in one of four identical cottages. Their neighbours, Bill O'Dwyer and Jim Burke lived in Land Commission houses, which had small farms and about twenty acres of land included. These houses stood on land acquired by the Free State after Irish Independence.

There was no television at that time. On a shelf near the front door sat a black, bakelite PYE valve radio. This had a dial showing 'exotic' radio stations such as Luxembourg, Paris, BBC Home and World Services and even Athlone. It was the source of great entertainment, with imaginative plays on a Sunday evening, live football and hurling matches from Croke Park commentated on by Michael O'Hehir, all on Radio Éireann.

Sean, as a younger boy, especially loved the stories told by Michael P. O'Connor at five o'clock in the late afternoon. Much imagination was required to listen to the radio and everyone had a different mind picture to everyone else, much the same as reading a book.

The young Noonans often tuned into Radio Luxembourg, to listen to pop music, especially on Saturday and Sunday evenings. They liked to hear who was going to be 'top of the pops' that week. Favourites were artists such as Ben E King (*Stand by Me*), Patsi Cline (*Crazy*) and Dion (*The Wanderer*). Kate, their mother, liked Elvis Presley (not the rock and roll stuff), Perry Como, the Irish tenor, Michael O'Duffy, the songs of Jim Reeves and the radio 'soap', *The Kennedys of Castleross*.

A popular Saturday night radio programme was *Take the Floor* hosted by Din Joe; all the family loved to listen to this. It was an Irish dance programme and very entertaining. Their father, Pat, liked it too but he did not like the 'yah-yah' stuff at all. He preferred to listen to his windup gramophone and enjoy '78' records by John McCormack and Father Sidney MacEwan.

Another favourite radio show was *The School around the Corner*, hosted by Paddy Crosby. It was often very funny, with children being children and speaking their minds. Paddy always got them to tell him about a 'funny incident', which could actually be a funny accident and at the end, there would be the bag of sweets to share. City children could embarrass their parents by mentioning things like 'hoppers' (fleas) being found in their beds.

The heavyweight boxing matches, broadcast from America, were a favourite on radio at that time. Brothers Dave and Mick would often get up very early to listen to matches, especially if they involved heroes such as Floyd Patterson fighting opponents: his arch-rival, Ingemar Johansson and later being defeated by Sonny Liston. Later on in the decade, there was the rise of Cassius Clay (Mohammad Ali).

On this particular morning – the first day of the holidays – Sean arose from his chair, having finished his breakfast of a fried egg together with some fried homemade brown bread. The brown bread was sometimes referred to as 'tear-arse' bread because of its anti-constipational properties. All this was washed down with a cup of tea with milk and sugar. His mother insisted on a breakfast been eaten every morning – good advice!

The sunshine made him feel happy. No more school for two months, he said to himself, just as a reminder. What shall I do today? he wondered. He had now almost outgrown his childhood games. Along with his brothers, Andy and Peader, he had invented two games: one was 'big yoke' and the second (very similar) 'little yoke'. They were both games involving vehicles (mostly cars and trucks) with a generous amount of imagination. Little yoke consisted of playing with whatever toy vehicles had survived the years, and was played either indoors or in the 'turf' shed. It didn't require much imagination and was usually played individually in separate areas. Toy cars or trucks were scarce and stones and sticks were sometimes employed with imagination. Big yoke, however, involved running up and down the yard and the road with pieces of wood or branches of young trees: and this is where the children's imaginations were employed to the full. Branches could be a Morris Minor, a Bedford truck or a Commer van. Sean now felt a bit embarrassed if he met a neighbour on the road, as he trotted along with a stick in his arms and he making vehicular noises.

Another game the boys played with their friend, Colm, was called 'Fire-ball hit', which was an obscure ball game with very relaxed rules. In fact, the rules were often made up as the game progressed. Andy sometimes got annoyed with this game and walked off in a huff.

On this, the first day of the holidays, Sean could smell the freshly tarred road, which had been resurfaced the day before and in years to come, that smell would bring back memories of happy days. A big red Bedford cattle lorry passed by, its creels creaking loudly and spilling some cow shite on the lovely road as it trundled along. He could see the silhouettes of the poor creatures on the truck, heading for the slaughterhouse most likely with nerves and fear causing the animals to scutter.

Bill O'Dwyer, Sean's neighbour, came cycling down the hill on his old, green, twin cross-barred bike. On the handlebar was a small, aluminium, rusted milk churn, which leaned against his chest. He wore a cap, an old grey suit and a collarless shirt. He also wore old turned down wellingtons, which had seen better days. Bill was heading for the pump to begin his day, drawing water for his thirsty cattle. He greeted Sean and added, "How many slaps did you get yesterday?"

Sean replied that he got none.

"What kind of school is that?!" retorted Bill.

One day, when Sean's mother, Katie, saw Bill passing with a full churn of water on the crossbar, she ran out and shouted, "Hey Bill."

Bill turned around and headed back to the cottage. Katie said, "Where would you be now if I hadn't called you?"

Bill did not see the joke and he headed back up the road, muttering under his breath.

Bill had a little farm up the road. It was quite small, only about twenty acres or so with another ten acres in a field about a mile away. He barely managed to maintain a moderate living out of this little farm. Life was not easy and the work was hard. He once advised Sean to stay away from the fields, as there was only hardship in them. Bill asked Sean and Peader to help him to take his cattle to Burton's yard. They were to be tested for tuberculosis. TB was a disease that the farmers dreaded. The loss of even one animal could prove disastrous. They worked hard getting the animals into the pen where the vet injected them. Afterwards, Bill gave each of them ten shillings and when they tried to refuse he said, 'Never refuse money in this life.'

Sean looked forward to August, when Bill would draw hay from his other field on his horse and bogey and he and his brothers and sister would ride on it. Some would sit at the front with Bill, while others sat on the space between the cock and the end of the bogey. This was a dangerous place as the bogey could tip up and trap a little leg or finger. It happened once with Sean's younger brother Andy, who was lucky only to suffer a black nail. Those sitting at the back had the job of calling to Bill when a car appeared from behind and space had to be made for it to pass. Cars were quite infrequent in the early sixties. Sometimes, Bill's father (nicknamed Cock for some obscure reason – or maybe not too obscure), would also ride up front on the bogey. Once he called out that lemonade was available and the children came running around, only to be disappointed to see the old horse having a good pee. When the bogey was not in use and tipped up, the children loved to use it as a slide. Care had to be taken to avoid getting a splinter up one's arse!

Jim Burke came cycling down the hill with his sheepdog, Rory, running along beside him. He was on his way to work in the large farm, about a mile from his home. As he approached the gate of the cottage where the spinsters, Annie and May Dillon, lived, his dog made a dash for it, knowing that their dog, Tiddles, would be waiting for him. A fierce row ensued through the wire of the gate, both dogs going full out for a fight. Annie came from the cottage door and threw a bucket of 'liquid' at Jim's dog, most of which got Jim. The actual content of the bucket was suspected not to be water! Jim made a few futile kicks at Tiddles, to the annoyance of the sisters, who wailed loudly.

This commotion happened most mornings and sometimes, in the evenings as well. Tiddles was a very spoiled pet and treated as a child by the unmarried sisters. He slept in their bed and was generally mollycoddled. Annie and May led simple lives. They enjoyed a smoke: Woodbines was their favourite cigarette brand and the cheapest on the market. Their 'staple' diet was 'an auld rasher' and boiled potatoes. Their house was as original as it was when built in the early Twentieth century, with an iron grate and the kettle hanging over the fire. They had a long hedge from their gate to the end of their garden along the road. One of the jobs in the summer months was to cut and trim it. This took them a good three weeks. Annie stood on a chair (they had no ladder) and trimmed it as best she could with the ancient clippers. May gathered up the trimmings. Every so often, they would retire to the house for a cup of tea and a smoke, which could take up to half an hour. They would laugh and joke with each other as Tiddles had a sleep nearby. Any neighbour passing by would be collared for a long chat, another excuse to stop working. However, when the hedge was eventually completed, it looked very well indeed.

Sean made his way up the gravel yard, where many a time he had grazed his knees and hands, to the garden. The two dogs, Rufus and Sweep (a cross wire-haired terrier and a black cross collie) ran to join him. They headed on up the garden to Sean's two brothers, Peader and Andy. An old Tiger Moth single engine bi-plane passed overhead. It was flying from the local airfield and was a common sight, especially at weekends. The local flying school had acquired half-a-dozen of these 1930/40 basic trainers when they became surplus after World War II. They used them in their school and were a common sight over Noonan's cottage. Also sighted, from time to time, was the odd Spitfire, also acquired from the RAF and operated by the Irish Air Corps. Another treat was to see the de Havilland Vampire jet trainers fly overhead on their way to Baldonnell. Yes, the jet age was here and this thrilled Sean. On a good day, he could sometimes see the vapour trails of a very high flying Boeing 707 or a DC8 on its way to the USA. He longed to fly on one, in the distant future when he would, at last, be a man.

A few years earlier, in 1957, the Russians had launched their satellite, *Sputnik*, into space. Sean had been amazed to see it pass overhead in the clear sky. It looked like a 'moving' star and all the boys found it very thrilling. He was saddened, however, when the Russians decided to send a live dog into space, which was doomed to die. However, the space age had arrived and the future was bright and challenging. In May 1960, the American U-2 spy plane was shot down over Russia and the pilot Gary Powers was captured. He was sentenced to a total of ten years in prison, including seven years hard labour. This worried Sean, as he heard his parents discussing the possibility of yet another world war. Gary Powers was released two years later in a prisoner exchange deal but the 'cold war' between Russia and the West continued. The Americans were disappointed that they were not the first to put a man into Space, which the Russians did when they launched Yuri Gagarin in April 1961. Alan Shepard was the first American to fly into Space in May that year. Sean went to see the American Space launches on his cousin's television on Saturday mornings. The black and white pictures showed billowing smoke and huge rockets disappearing into the sky. It was all so exhilarating!

Adventures and the Dispossessed

The boys decided to go on an adventure this day to the nearby wood. The dogs would come with them. The wood, which stood on about ten acres, was surrounded in the lower part by tall pine trees. A variety of wild vegetation: brambles, nettles, young ash plants etc. covered the centre of this part. The upper part consisted of pine trees and was easier to get through. They planned to make their way from the lower to the upper part, where, at the end of the boundary, stood the big house where the owners of the large farm lived.

The big house had ten bedrooms, a couple of reception rooms, a kitchen, three bathrooms and various out-houses. The estate had been far larger when it had been owned by the 'Ascendancy' than it was now. The original family moved out after the birth of the Free State (which led to the Irish Republic) and the Land Commission had acquired much of the land. The farm now only employed two men; whereas perhaps ten to fifteen men would have worked there in years past.

The boys liked to try to sneak up to the house without being spotted by one of the men; if they were seen, they would make a run for it. There was no sign of the workmen today and they looked at the manor house through the laurel hedge, which grew about twenty yards across the yard from it. Mrs Kelly's car was parked to the left of the big green front door with the half circle skylight.

Andy whispered, "I bet one of you a shilling that you won't run to the door and knock the knocker."

Sean said, "You haven't got a shilling, Andy."

"Well sixpence then."

"You haven't a tanner either; have you?"

"I will on Saturday when I do the messages."

Peader thought the idea daft and kept his mouth shut but Sean agreed to go. He slipped along the side of the hedge, crossed the narrow roadway and he was now at the right gable of the house. He peeped around the corner and could see the entrance along the creeper clad front elevation. The sixpence was his!

He tiptoed towards his goal, ducked under three of the front windows and approached the fourth when the front door opened. Sean froze! Mrs Kelly's foot appeared on the step, clad in a black leather boot, followed by the rest of her person, clad in a fur coat and matching hat. Luckily for Sean, her back was towards him and he thawed and sidled back to the gable end. The good lady of the manor lowered herself into the large Vauxhall, backed away from the house and drove off along the avenue. Sean sneaked back to his awaiting brothers, who insinuated that he was a coward. Sean pointed out that if no one was at home there was no point in knocking the knocker. He had planned to knock on the door and run for cover at the other side of the car if the door opened quickly. Anyway, there would be no sixpence for him on Saturday.

The Kelly family lived in the large house. They were Catholics and they farmed the 300 acres of land quite successfully. They only employed two full-time labourers and, in the summer, they employed several casual labourers. One of these casual workers was a well-known man-of-the-road known as 'Madman' Murray. James Murray was said to come from a neighbouring town and had run away with 'travelling people' when he was a young teenager. He had a lump on the crown of his head, which was said to have been the result of a whack from a metal object – perhaps a large pot or frying pan – administered by an irate travelling person. Perhaps there was an argument over a young lady or was it in a drunken brawl? No one knew for sure. At any rate, his 'madness' was blamed on this lump.

One day Sean was in the yard, playing with some toy soldiers when he heard a man hollering loudly as he was coming down the road. The noise became nearer and nearer. His mother also heard the racket and came out of the house. Jim Murray came into view: his head wet from washing it under the pump; his dirty collarless shirt open; his ragged jacket bulging with various personal items; his ragged-arsed trousers tucked into his patched up wellies and his bundle under his arm. The large lump protruded from the top of Jim's bald head and appeared to be redder than usual.

Kate called for Jim to calm down:

"Jim, Jim what's the matter?"

"That bloody bitch, who does she think I am? Insulting me with only a tanner and all the money she has. The stuck up floosey!"

With that, he threw the shiny coin on the ground. Kate picked it up and looked at it.

"Hey Jim, that's a shilling, not a sixpence."

She handed it back to poor Jim, who had begun to calm down. Mrs Burton had given him the coin, either for some work done or as a gift. Jim looked carefully at the coin and decided that it was a shilling after all. He seemed to calm down a little.

"Come in and have a cup of tea Jim."

"Thanks Missus, I will. You can't bate a cuppa tay."

Jim often came in for 'tay' and chatted away quite sensibly. He liked to talk about football and the Kildare team. "Di ya think she'll win on Sunday?" he would ask, referring to the team's next match in Croke Park. He hated the law in the embodiment of 'an auld guard' and all they stood for. Sometimes, he would come from Kelly's house across the field and would be giving out hell about that family or its employees. He would cross the 'bars' at the end of the garden and head down to Noonan's house. If he came across an egg in the garden, dropped by an inexperienced pullet, he would carefully pick it up and bring it to Kate Noonan. He was very honest man indeed!

He was well in his fifties now and was feeling his age a bit. Sleeping rough also did not help. His days as a casual labourer were nearing their end. Sometimes, he would be upset when one of the workers 'asked' him to leave his 'comfortable' bed in the hay barn. He was also upset by the new generation of housewives. They did not invite him in for tea: most were frightened of him, since he looked very scruffy and smelled not a little. Jim complained to Kate one day, saying Missus 'Turf' had sent him away. Missus 'Turf' was a woman who came from a house near a Donadea bog.

Jim was one of several 'men of the road' who roamed the roads of Kildare and Meath. They were the 'dispossessed' who had fallen on hard times and mental ill-health. Jim Murray would continue wandering the countryside, getting tea here, a meal there and rest wherever he could find it. It was a tough life but he knew no other. There were farmers and families, including the Noonans, who he could depend upon to look after him. He avoided the towns, as often he came in for abuse from the townies, who jeered and made fun of him. Jim's life would eventually end when he was knocked down by a car while crossing a busy road. The increase in traffic was a great problem for him and it took his life. He had a huge funeral; all paid for by the local people.

Other regular visitors to the neighbourhood were the 'travelling people', whose piebald horses appeared over the hill, drawing their wooden caravans with all the family on board and the dogs trailing behind, tied to the vehicles. They often made their camp down the road, on the 'two corners', staying for many days. They cooked over an open fire and Sean was often afraid when passing by at night on his bicycle. The men looked fearsome as they drank, smoked and chatted loudly by the fire. Some of the women joined them, drinking Guinness from bottles and sometimes a singsong began and, later perhaps, a row. Usually the womenfolk with young children knocked on doors begging for tea, sugar, bread and something for the 'little wans'. There was hardly ever any trouble but sometimes a gate to a field was opened and the horses let it to graze. The local farmer would remonstrate with them and words would be exchanged. Many neighbours ensured all their sheds and houses were locked, in case of a visit by an unscrupulous traveller. The 'travellers' were never welcome in the local public houses; they were barred from many. They could be good customers but trouble often flared up when they over imbibed. Many a bar was wrecked because too much drink was sold to them by greedy landlords.

These were tough people, who were also members of the 'dispossessed' and this was the only life they knew. They received little, if any education and felt rejected by the population. Without a settled address and education, life looked very bleak for most of them. Many died young due to their hard life, living mostly in the open air and without access to medical facilities.

Sheila Kelly was a very kind woman. If she drove down the road before school time and came across the Noonan children heading for the bus stop, she would offer them a lift if she was going to town. She drove a new Vauxhall Velox, which Sean loved. It smelled of newness and the bench seats were red leather. It was styled on American cars with lots of chrome and fins at the back, a 'column' gear change and a big silver horn, which was almost the size of the steering wheel itself.

Sheila had married Cornelius Kelly when she was twenty-one and came from County Meath to live in the large Kelly house. She had grown up on a largish farm, so she knew quite a lot about farming. The Kelly house proved to be quite a challenge, as Corney's mother was now growing old and spent most of her time in her room, or in the front reception room. They had a maid and a cook but the running of the house was now Sheila's responsibility. Her mother-in-law would sometimes try to interfere but Sheila was a diplomat and managed to persuade the old lady to see things from her point of view.

The old wood was magical to Sean. The old oak tree there reminded him of the film *Darby O'Gill and the Little People*. In it, Jimmy O'Dea played a large leprechaun, who, being the King of the Fairies, would disappear through a door at the base of a similar oak tree and, running down a spiral staircase, enter the Great Hall of the fairies, where dancing, music and merriment continued through the night. Sean imagined himself following 'Darby' down and taking part in all the fun. Sean's father used to tell him stories of leprechauns and 'coshapookas' and he told him he often heard the 'tap, tap, tap' of leprechauns working at their trade as cobblers.

Also in the wood was a small clearing, at the end of which were young ash plants sprouting up, competing for the light. The boys imagined it to be a fortress and named it 'Daddilly-Dumpa'. They had names on different parts of the wood, like Charing Cross and Camelot. They built a 'den' of wild rhubarb leaves and young saplings and often spent the whole day there.

On the way home, the boys stopped at the large cattle trough at the top of the field and searched for 'pinkeens' – the name they gave tadpoles. They often brought jam jars and fished out the baby frogs to bring them home. Sometimes, they captured a frog and kept it under a bucket in the yard. Next morning, they were disappointed to find it gone, not knowing that their father had set it free.

Another source of adventure for the boys was the Obelisk: an Eighteenth century folly, which was in poor repair. Their mother warned them not to climb up the dangerous stairs but the boys dared each other to go, and up they went. Some of the steps were missing and there were no rails to stop a boy from falling off but the scenery from the balcony of the middle chamber was wonderful. Noonan's house could be seen to the north and Castletown House to the south. The folly consisted of three arches, with a stairway to the chamber above the middle arch. Above the two side arches, two smaller arches stood with a small column and a stone pineapple on top. Above the higher chamber the 'Obelisk' towered to 175 feet. Stones were missing from the tower and they lay around the ground while ivy crawled up the sides of the arches. The structure stood on about two acres of land, most of which was overgrown. Iron railings enclosed the whole area but nature had almost smothered these in briars and shrubs. These were a wonderful source of blackberries for the local children, who often gorged themselves while supposed to be picking them for their mothers to make delicious jam.

This monstrous monument to ascendency, poverty and famine built by Lady Conolly, widow of Speaker Conolly, was to 'adorn her estate and honour her husband'. It was a disaster from the beginning. Aidan Higgins described it as 'the preposterous Obelisk'. It cost Lady Louisa £400, with labour at a halfpenny a day. It was believed that the good Lady had commissioned it to relieve a local famine. In any case, Sean and his brothers loved to play in and around it: being soldiers in a war, or knights in armour riding white steeds, or even cowboys and Indians. They kept it secret from their parents. The secret was part of the adventure.

The Obelisk was also a place of ghosts and ghouls: at least that is what Mick Noonan told his siblings. He told of men walking past the huge edifice at night and hearing an invisible 'being' coming behind, dragging a ghostly chain along the stony lane. This often turned out to be an unleashed goat curiously following the traveller. Sean never liked to pass the place after dark. One winter's night, Mick dared his brother, Tom, to climb up the dark and often slippery stairs to the top chamber on his own. Tom said that, "it wouldn't be a problem" and asked when he should go.

"Now", said Mick. "Yeah, off you go, Now, Tom!"

The night was very dark and the moon was hidden behind the dark, gloomy clouds. In spite of all this, Tom threw on his coat and went to get his bike.

Mick asked, "How will I know you climbed to the top?"

"You'll just have to trust me Mick."

Mick thought about what the adventure entailed. Would Tom slip and fall going up the stairs or, even worse, fall from the top? He would never live it down or be forgiven by the family.

"Ok, Ok Tom, I believe you would do it. It's a cold dark night so let's leave it for another time"

When a warm spell of weather came – which was not very often – the children were allowed to go for a swim in the canal or the local river. Swimming wear was in short supply and old, ill-fitting underwear was used. Few of them could actually swim, however, they enjoyed splashing about in the water and drenching each other. Sean, Andy and Peader were members of the non-swimmers club and were happy to splash about among the reeds and spot the occasional minnow dashing past in the clear water.

At weekends, the hard boys from the town ventured out to the bridge and were eager to show off to the 'country' boys and especially the 'country' girls. Mary Noonan was numbered among the latter. The 'country' boys also wanted to impress the girls and often dared their rivals to perform a heroic feat. Paddy Keenan dared everyone to jump off the bridge into the canal. No one challenged him and he was forced to perform the feat himself.

Up he went to the top of the bridge. He was not a swimmer but he didn't care. He gingerly climbed up on the wall, desperately trying to conceal the fear that had suddenly assailed him but luckily, he was a good actor. Standing on the wall, he flexed his muscles and taunted the townies. He suddenly let out a Tarzan-like roar and dived towards the water, to the cheers of the crowd. The dive developed into an enormous belly-flop as he hit the water, disappeared beneath the surface and narrowly escaped suffering a critical injury as he scraped his chest off the stony bottom. All watched in awe and were relieved when his head appeared, revealing a smiling, triumphant face but soon, his bleeding chest was visible; the girls gasped and some ran to help him out of the canal. He was given a hero's welcome as he climbed onto the bank and enjoyed the attention of the boys and, especially, the girls.

Paddy always played the big hero in everything he did: football, cycling, whatever. He dared other lads to do the same but they refused and the townies jumped into the canal shouting and splashing, trying desperately to defuse the situation and win back the attention of the girls. The country boys had won the day!

Dave Noonan nearly drowned in the canal one day. He was unable to swim and, slipping into a hole, he went out of his depth. He went under, resurfaced, went under again. Fortunately, his brother Mick happened to be close at hand and pulled him up; gasping, coughing, sputtering and spitting out water. Dave was stressed out, having swallowed a large amount of not exactly clean canal water but all were warned not to tell the parents. He sat on the bank, hugging a towel and after a while, was feeling himself again. Other times, the boys cycled to the local river, which was nearer the town and had a swim. Some of the lads did not like going there as the current was often a little strong and the town boys often outnumbered them. No one ever drowned there but there were quite a few near misses.

The long summer holidays promised many a day full of adventure, or so it seemed to Sean on this, the first day.

The Messages

Sean and Peadar took turn to go to the town to get the 'messages' on Saturday morning. Sean's bike was a bit ancient. His father sourced bicycles for his children from various places and people. He got a frame from here and a wheel from there but usually, he built a decent bike. A selection of bicycles was parked against the gable of the cottage and sometimes it was difficult to find the required one. Some of Sean's brothers would simply ride through the gate and let the bike park itself, much to their father's annoyance.

The sky looked ominous as Sean got ready for his journey, so he donned his raincoat. This was a black hand-me-down and was full length on him, although it was supposed to be three-quarter length. It covered his knees, which was welcome, as he had not yet progressed to long trousers. He put a rain hat on and his wellingtons (also referred to as top-boots), making a perfectly ridiculous figure. The combination of short trousers and wellies often caused his legs to become sore in the wet and cold weather, making the winter even more uncomfortable. On his way to the town, Sean was obliged to call to two neighbours to see if they wanted anything. They were Bill O'Dwyer's sister, Josie Farrell, and Jim Burke's wife Angela. Josie would hand Sean a purse with a list of items to be purchased and a pound note. She would say to him, "Go easy on that pound." Angela would also give him a list and a purse. So he had three purses and several lists for different shops. A bit of a nightmare!

On the way to town, he passed the time by imagining that he was driving a 1950's Chevrolet that he had seen in some film in the convent. It had a split windscreen and lashings of chrome, including a massive grill sporting the Chevrolet logo. The seats were made of red leather, like Mrs Kelly's Velox, and the dashboard had many 'clocks', including the speedometer and a large radio playing the latest hits very loud. Then he would imagine he was driving a large Bedford truck, red in colour with double wheels at the back and a tipper trailer.

The Presentation Sisters ran the convent in town, which had been built in the nineteenth century. The nuns were not an enclosed order. They taught primary school girls up to Sixth Class. They also taught boys and girls in both the little and big 'Babies' and also a mysterious class between the big 'Babies' and First Class, known as 'High Middle Division'. It was a kind of Purgatory for children who were too big for the lower class and not advanced enough for the First Class. Sean had quite enjoyed these classes and remembered his time in 'High Middle Division' as a very relaxed time.

The old Reverend Mother, Mother Alphonsus, would come from the depths of the convent, appearing as if from the cupboard, heading, with her rosary beads rattling, for First Class. Woe betide the boy or girl in the nearest desk to the door who didn't jump up and open it, as they would get a good whack of the beads or a ruler. The nuns, and many national school teachers, took exception to their students writing with their left hand and widely discouraged it. Boys and girls were often beaten with a ruler on the left hand and told, in no uncertain terms, to use the right. It even happened that a student's left hand was tied behind his or her back, in one of the more extreme measures employed to discourage this 'sinister' practice.

Sean was very confused the first time he went to school at the convent. On his first day, his mother brought him in on the bus. They walked to the Dublin road, passed Brennan's, Farrell's and Burke's and the lonely wood. In winter the wood shaded the road making it liable to frost and ice, which made it dangerous. It was always dreary in winter and still shaded in the summer. Finally, they crossed the railway/canal bridge and arrived at the bus stop. They waited on the main road for the bus. Sean secretly hoped it would never come. However, soon the big, green Leyland double-decker appeared over the hill, swaying from side to side on the uneven road. They boarded it through the open back door and made their way to the long seat at the front. Sean liked this seat as he could see the driver in his cab and marvelled at his skill in manoeuvring the large vehicle. Having descended from the bus, they made their way to the school.

Mammy brought Sean through the big green wooden door, which led across the small concrete yard. Sister Agnes of the Presentation Sisters greeted them, as well as all the other 'little' infants starting that day. The nun was a small, red-faced woman in her early fifties who smiled at the children and their mothers and made them feel at ease. The children howled and bawled when the time came for parting and Sean was no exception. He clung to his mother, looking fearfully at the kind nun. However, soon all the mothers were gone and there Sean was, with his new classmates and the happy-faced nun. However, he was unsure what this creature was. She wore a black habit right to the floor. A wimple covered her head and neck and her face was cradled in a white, cardboard-like item, which also went across her forehead. The same material descended from under her chin to just below her breasts. Was she a man or a woman? He wasn't sure. Maybe there was a third sex!

In later years, in the summer months, it was traditional for a seven-aside football tournament to be held in the convent grounds. There was a field suited to the game not far from the convent buildings. In between, there was a well laid out garden and inside this was the nuns' final resting place. The latter had rows of crosses for the deceased nuns, together with larger crosses for the Reverend Mothers. There was a statue of Our Lady, attired as the Queen of Heaven, overlooking the 'narrow cells'. When the games took place on summer evenings, Sean would notice some of the younger nuns at the windows enjoying the football. They were not allowed to come closer. In later life, Sean wondered what these women, some only young girls, were thinking. Did they regret their life dedicated to God and far remote from family life? Did they allow themselves to ponder about nature and their innate desire to have children and live a 'normal' life? A life given to God is something between the person and his or her Maker: never to be understood by those who remain in the 'World'.

The seven-aside football tournament was looked forward to every year. All the neighbouring towns and villages were asked to choose a team and enter the competition. Of course, the best men were selected, together with several 'subs'. Some of the better teams even had the luxury of having inter-county players. Players were often from several counties as the town was not very far from at least three. There were no changing rooms and players had to make do undressing and donning their togs and shirts and boots behind an open car door, or a friendly hedge with not too many briars and nettles. There were no toilet facilities and definitely no chance of a shower, except that provided by nature. After the games, the stench of sweat was very strong and then again, few had the luxury of a bathroom at home. Washing was only done on a Saturday night in many homes. The good nuns must have been forced to avert their eyes should some player remove his shirt or (God forbid!) drop his trousers in their line of sight.

The long summer evenings were ideal for the seven-a-side tournament. The first rounds took place during the week and a good attendance was usual. The town folk loved sport and the matches were tough and fast. As the tournament progressed, the matches got better and the attendance increased. The finals were held at the weekends and these were really thrilling.

It must be said, however, that these matches were taken very seriously and sometimes degenerated into a free-for-all punch-up. Spectators often joined in the rows and Sean was present when a notorious fight erupted one Friday evening. It was a semi-final and the local team was playing one of their nearest neighbours. There was a lot of rivalry and the two towns were old football enemies, so many spectators only came to see the fight, the match just added to the entertainment.

Two players fought hard to gain possession of the ball near the sideline. The player from the 'other' town gave the local lad a hefty shoulder, followed by a sneaky kick to the back of the knee. Retaliation followed with a smack to the jaw and another 'foreign' player landed a fist to the local lad's ear. In a split second, several players joined in and two rolled into the crowd. This was the signal for the 'free-for-all' and the spectators dutifully joined in.

The poor referee hadn't a chance and soon, the pitch was a battlefield with fists flying and noses bleeding and spectacles being flung in all directions. The recently retired Garda officer, Dinney Breeney, wading in to try to break up the fight, was greeted with a well-placed slap to the jaw. His false teeth went flying into a warring party, only to be trampled underfoot. Women also joined in the mêlée, employing handbags and umbrellas as weapons of war. The match had to be abandoned and arrangements made for a replay. The nuns watching the games from their windows would, at this point, close the windows and curtains, resume their prayers or simply retire to bed.

The nuns also operated a laundry during the week. May Dillon was employed there and a lot of the items they washed and cleaned came from the seminary at the other end of the town. The priests and student priests wore only black clerical clothes and white shirts and underclothes – including long johns. She once suffered a severe burn from an iron and was off work for several weeks. There was no compensation to be had.

At weekends, they turned the laundry into a cinema – or picture house as it was best known. Sean went there on Sunday afternoons, mostly in the autumn and winter. The film would start at 3pm with the 'serial' film, which continued from week to week, or a 'B' film. It often featured a car-racing event and Sean found it fascinating. The main feature was the best: usually a cowboy film starring Gene Autry or John Wayne. The John Wayne films often had that magnificent backdrop of Monument Valley in Arizona. Sean enjoyed watching the poor old Indians being shot to pieces. Genocide was not a word he was familiar with! Other favourites were Roy Rodgers and his beautiful horse, Trigger; not to forget the Lone Ranger and his faithful sidekick, Tonto. Everything in America seemed wonderful to Sean.

A certain family in the town often had only one four pence admittance fee. One of the boys would be chosen and given the money, with which he would enter. When the lights were off and the 'B' film started, the chosen boy would unlock the 'exit' doors and the rest of the gang would sneak in. However, Sister Bernard, when on duty, copped on to the scam and immediately locked the door while scanning the audience for the perpetrators. These would quickly mingle with the crowd and the good sister would again fail in her duty.

Once Sean and two of his brothers came in late to the picture house and the change from the light into the dark disoriented and partially blinded them. Peader stretched out his hands to feel his way in, poking an unsuspecting punter in the face, almost gouging his eyes out and fondling another poor girl in the breast area. It must have been a bit of a shock to see three country lads coming in and approaching with arms out-stretched. Luckily, their eyes soon adjusted to the dark and the three boys found a seat.

Sister Bernard was very active at the late Saturday night show. Lovers were expected to hold hands only whilst sitting very close together: kissing was definitely a no-no! The good sister would shine her torch in all directions, reminiscent of a wartime search light, ensuring good behaviour was strictly adhered to. No one wanted their faces lit up for all to see, especially if they happened to be stealing a sly kiss.

After the 'matinée' on a Sunday afternoon in winter, Sean would come from the 'cinema' full of the character he had just seen on the silver screen. He could be Roy Rodgers on his horse Trigger, or John Wayne the cavalry officer. He would ride his bike (now a horse) and gallop up the road, fearless and ready to face any danger. However, when a Garda stopped him and asked why he had no lights on his bike he nearly shit himself.

On this particular shopping trip into town, he continued cycling along the road, dreaming his dreams about driving this American car. He checked from time to time to see if the purses were still in their separate pockets. The clouds began to gather on the horizon. Two blackbirds squabbled in the hedgerow and a flock of crows headed over the distant trees, cawing as they flew. He approached one of Jim Burke's workmates, who was busy cutting a roadside hedge. This was an art in itself. The partly cut branches had to be laid together and the surplus ones removed. Later, the laid branches would sprout and form a solid barrier to keep the cattle in. Tommy Clark spotted Sean cycling toward him:

"Hi Sean. How is things?"

"Not too bad thanks, Tommy, and how are you?'

"Ah, hanging on in there. Can you get me a packet of ten fags in the town? Carroll's tipped please."

"Sure Tommy. How much are they?"

"There's two bob. Don't be long, I'm gaspin'. Don't forget the change."

Sean continued on to the crossroads and turned right towards the town. Going to town was good as it was downhill. Coming back was a different matter, especially if the wind was in your face! He cycled past the fields, where he observed rabbits feeding noiselessly in the lonely fields and heard a cock pheasant calling loudly to his mate. He passed Tomlinson's twin stone-pillared gateway.

The Tomlinson's were a Protestant couple who owned quite a large farm and lived in a large farmhouse about a half a mile down a tree-lined avenue. They had no children and Susana Tomlinson drove a black split-screened 1953 Morris Minor – badly. She revved up the engine well in excess of the required level, nearly red-lining it (if it had a rev counter), before she moved off and then kept the poor car in equally high revs as the gears were changed or crunched upwards. However, in the early sixties, very few women could drive a car so it was supposed her tutor was, perhaps, not the best in the world. Approaching November, Susana would call to the local houses and try to sell a poppy at each call. Poppies were not popular as they raised funds for British soldiers and many would frown upon such a cause in the Irish Republic of the 1950/60s. However, thousands of Irish men fought and died for Britain and freedom, in both World Wars and this was conveniently forgotten by most at that time.

In Flanders Fields

In Flanders fields, the poppies grow
Through the crosses, row on row,
That mark our place and in the sky,
The larks, still bravely singing, fly.
Scarce heard amid the guns below

We are the Dead. Short days ago
We lived, felt dawn, saw sunset glow,
Loved and were loved, and now we lie
In Flanders fields.

– John McCrae, May 1915

Sean's older brother, Dave, worked as a farm labourer for the Tomlinsons. Joe McGuire, who lived in the cottage next to Sean's, also worked there before he retired. He used to borrow his employer's ass to get some coal and heavier 'messages' from the town. However, when the ass approached the gates, he refused to continue on straight to the town. Instead, he insisted on turning left into the avenue, all the way to the farmyard, turn around and head back down the avenue. Only then would he turn right towards the town.

One of the local lads once walked from the town to Tomlinson's to ask for a job. The Tomlinsons were then newly married and Susana answered the tradesman's door. The young man was well built but with a small frame and stature. Mrs Tomlinson enquired if he was a jockey. "No," he replied but added that he could "do with a mount." He did not get a job.

Joe McGuire was character who lived, with his spinster daughter, in his cottage and was already retired in 1961. He smoked a pipe with a lid on it and usually, it was upside down. He always wore a jacket, waistcoat and a cap. On Sundays, he sported a fine pocket watch in the waistcoat. In those days, men wore either a hat or a cap and it was only in the chapel on Sunday that one could see who had or hadn't hair. He loved to puff on his pipe while having a chat across the fence with Sean's father, Pat. Pat Noonan was a hat man. They would reminisce about years gone by and often mentioned the spectacular lightening display during a thunderstorm in 1911. They also remarked about the youth of the day. Joe McGuire was flabbergasted one day when he saw a young lad take a comb from his pocket and 'racked his hair' in public.

Pat also enjoyed his pipe. Lighting a pipe was a ritual in itself. First, the pipe had to be cleaned with a cleaner and the old tobacco scooped out of the bowl with a penknife. Then there was the 'plug' of tobacco. Pat preferred Yachtsman. The plug had to be cut with a penknife, then the pieces of tobacco were rolled in the palm of the hand until it became pliable. It was then fed into the pipe. A succession of matches were lit and applied until the smoker was happy with the draw and only then could the tobacco be enjoyed.

When Joe McGuire called to the Noonan's house he would always call out, "God save all here" to be answered with, "You too Joe".

He was a very friendly character and was never offensive. His only weakness was that every six months, he would 'go on the beer' and spend a solid fortnight on the tear. It stemmed from a time when he worked as a farm labourer and was paid quarterly. When he got the money, he would head for the pub and go on the batter. In his latter days, his binges became less frequent and sense came with old age.

He owned an old 'ladies' Raleigh bicycle, which he used to go to the town. He wore a long black overcoat when he went cycling and made sure he lit up his pipe for the journey. He would puff it merrily whilst cycling, very slowly, along the road. Sean once saw him approach the hill near his house from the other side. As he neared the summit, the bike slowed and slowed and then, whilst almost making it, it stalled and Mick fell sideways, crossing the grass verge and ending up in the ditch. Puffs of smoke appeared from the ditch before Mick reappeared, unscathed if a little shaken.

When Sean finally obtained long trousers, Joe McGuire was the first to wish him, "Long may you wear a mhic." The term 'a mhic' (a vick) was from the Irish meaning, 'my son' or 'son'.

*****

Sean turned right at the 'fingerpost', where the countryside began to change into a town. The houses became closer to one another and even a footpath appeared at the side of the road. He approached the old railway station on his left. This was now merely a signal box overlooking twin tracks, where the intercity trains swopped over the 'staff', which was required for one train to continue on the single line to the next point. The station had been a busy place in years gone by, before the motorcar and the motor buses became king. There was a railway hotel in the town, which still existed but was no longer a place where clients could find bed and board. In the words of Percy French, when it was a hotel, "it was often difficult to determine which was the bed, and which was the board!"

The ancient canal ran parallel to the railway line and Sean noticed some waterfowl and their chicks dashing here and there in the shallow water, while a kingfisher dived from a branch to collect his dinner from the canal. He cycled the last hundred yards to the square and Main Street.

The Square was lined on one side by one of the five public houses of the town and on the other, by a large town house and the bookmakers shop. Facing Main Street at the back of the Square was a large house, which was once an R.I.C. barracks. The Square once had a 'town hall' in its centre but the IRA torched it during the War of Independence. In 1961 the centre was an ad hoc parking place for town shoppers.

Sean's first stop was a small grocer's shop to the left of the Square across the street. His mother bought some items there, as they were friends of the family. Dermot and Alice Cusack ran the small shop, which had only a short but very high counter (to an eleven-and-a-half-year-old boy at least) and they even employed a shop girl. She did most of the serving while Alice often helped out, looking for items etc. Then he went to a larger grocer at the end of the street and bought groceries for all three clients. Sean's father had an 'account' or 'slate' there and the items on the list were added to it. The items for the other two women were paid for in cash and the change carefully returned to the different purses. Sometimes Sean would be given money to take off the bill.

This larger shop had yet another high counter, which ran much further than the former. Three shop assistants served the customers. This was before the first supermarket came to the town in the late sixties. A list was given to an assistant, who assembled the items on top of the counter. Many items, such as sugar and some tea, came in brown bags. The customer was charged by the weight and there was little choice given, unless the customer asked for a particular brand. This also happened when

Sean would be required to leave in a list on a Wednesday afternoon or a Thursday morning for the main shopping, which was delivered to the house on a Friday evening. His mother would simply list the items required and it was up to the assistant to assemble them in a large cardboard box. There was a lot of trust required, as no prices were available. The cardboard box was a great plaything when Sean was younger. He and his younger brother would play with it for hours. It could be a bus, an airplane, a house or anything they wanted it to be.

Sean, like most boys of his age and stature, was usually bullied by the local housewives in these shops. This especially happened in the butcher's shop: the last call due to the perishability of its products. The local butcher, Jimmy O'Neill, would chat up the women when they came to his shop, especially the younger ones. He would tease them about lumps of meat and when they last had one (which went over Sean's head) and about subtle love affairs and even toilet issues, or the lack of. Sean would stand, desperately trying to get his attention, until a kind old lady would speak up for him.

After visiting all of the required shops, it was time to make his way back home, with the bicycle fully loaded. It was difficult to cycle, especially into the wind with bags hopping off his bare knees. Sometimes, a large lorry would pass him, quite close, causing him to wobble and there were times when he would lose something from a bag and have to stop and walk back to get it.

*****

The ten cigarettes were handed over to Tommy Clark (who was still cutting the hedge) together with the two pence change. He thanked Sean and asked if he had a light. Sean didn't have a match and a box of matches cost two pence. Why did Tommy not ask for a box when Sean was heading for town? Sean asked him if he was broke.

"No," Tommy said "but I am badly bent."

After all his trouble, Sean got a shilling tip that day from Josie Farrell. He was delighted. It meant he could buy two sixpenny bars of Cadbury chocolate, or even one large shilling bar. The shilling bar was a glutton's delight and he could feast on it for ages. It was on one of these grocery trips that Sean tasted crisps for the first time. It was a packet of 'Tayto' cheese and onion flavour and they tasted divine. The packet cost four pence but later, he discovered he could buy a packet of 'Perry' crisps for three pence (or 'thruppence' as the coin was affectionately called). However, he much preferred the 'Tayto' brand.

Doon na Ree

One day, during the holidays, Sean, Peader and Andy decided to have a picnic in a place they called Doon na Ree (after the popular song of the day sung by Ruby Murray). They scraped up what money they had and Peader went in to the town to buy lemonade and biscuits, then they headed off with the dogs through the fields, towards the railway line and canal.

They crossed several fields on a beaten path, crossing what was once an ornate gateway to a big house, long demolished. The piers were still intact but the gates were well rusted and bent. The gateway was 'fenced' with old bushes cut from a hedge but the boys managed to squeeze through a space beside one of the piers. As they crossed the second field, they could make out the ruins of a once elegant farmhouse. The remaining walls were covered with ivy and most of the roof had caved in. The only dwellers of the former family home were some rooks and a few pigeons, who now quarrelled over the best nesting sites. In the walled farmyard, there was an old house in which a family still lived. There were some outbuildings still standing. It was said that the family who lived in the big house were virtually wiped out, from 1918 to 1920, by TB and they were forced to leave it following the deaths of their teenage children.

The three boys carried on to another ruin of once ornate gates and on to a partly wooded area, which would take them up a small hill to Doon na Ree. From the top of the little hill, they could view the railway line and the old canal, now much overgrown with lily pads and reeds. They could see a heron dodge through the latter and secure a welcome lunch of a frog in the water. Waterfowl busily searched the same waters for their sustenance, chirping and calling to each other as they manoeuvred through the vegetation. Young chicks swam around excitedly whilst their mothers watched them jealously. The boys watched the railway signal, which told, when it was down, of an advancing train and they waited eagerly to see what type of train would pass along the track.

It reminded Sean of a time, several years earlier, when his elder sister Mary would bring himself and his brothers for a walk to the old bridge, which spanned both the railway and the canal. There, they would wait and see one of the last steam engines approach and pass below. They would see it sending smoke up one side of the bridge and, running across, they would see smoke rising from the other side. The steam trains were fascinating and Sean saw them at a transition period, when CIÉ were gradually introducing diesel trains. From the Noonan's, the puffing smoke of a steam engine, pulling freight carriages and heading west from Dublin, could often be seen making its weary way along the line on a still and tranquil summer evening in the 1950's.

The boys could see the spire of St Patrick's College from Doon na Ree. The clock chimed every quarter, half and full hour. It was their only way of keeping track of time: only very rich children sported a watch.

At last, the train appeared and sounded its whistle as it approached the signal. The driver waved to the boys. It was a diesel and had five passenger carriages and a guard's van at the rear. The boys looked eagerly at the passengers, to see if they recognised any of them but, of course, they didn't.

At the top of the hill of Doon na Ree, the boys settled down and opened the 'picnic'. They enjoyed the lemonade and biscuits and talked about what the future would hold for them. They had wonderful dreams of being a pilot or a headmaster or even, a very famous singer. Anything was possible; their imaginations ran wild.

As they chatted, the Angelus bell rang out from the local church, or 'chapel' as it was mostly known. 'Church' was a term mostly reserved for a Protestant or Church of Ireland building, whilst 'Chapel' usually referred to a Catholic building. Sean's mother used to ask, while out for a Sunday drive, "Is that a church or a chapel?"

It was also a sin for a Catholic to enter a Protestant church. Sean's mother was once asked to the wedding of her non-Catholic friend when they worked in a big house in the 1930's. She had to ask the priest, in Confession, for permission to go. The priest eventually relented but warned her not to participate in the service in any way. Sean's cousin told the story of throwing a fellow schoolboy's cap through the open door of the local 'church'. He watched it skidding down the aisle and dared the owner to go and get it, knowing that he was going to commit a sin by doing so.

The boys dutifully recited the Angelus as the bell tolled in the distance: *The angel of the Lord declared onto Mary, and she conceived of the Holy Ghost ...*

When the prayers were said, they headed back home with the dogs, through the little wood and across by the old farmhouse and along the beaten path to the house and a lovely 'tea' made by the Mammy.

The Little Farm

In early July, the three boys, Sean, Peader and Andy were required to head to the family field, to start the arduous task of thinning the turnips and mangolds. In March, Dermot Hyland (a friend of Dave Noonan) had ploughed and harrowed the field using a tractor borrowed from the Vauxhall/Bedford Main dealer in the town. Drills were then made and some were reserved for potatoes and the rest for turnips and mangolds.

The mangold crop was grown as cattle feed in the winter. The seeds were sown in May/June and by early July, they were ready for thinning. A gap of about four to six inches was left between the plants and weeds were removed at this stage. The three boys were expected to work a drill each. The plants would be quite small but the weeds would be well established. As they worked their way along the drills, they would be tormented by flies breeding in the weeds. They would also have to dodge the showers and take shelter under a hedge or tree. Again, none of the boys possessed a watch. The college steeple clock was now too far away to hear, so they had to guess the time. They looked at the sun, when it was visible and tried to work out the time and failed hopelessly. After what seemed like hours and hours of labour, they would head home across the fields.

Sometimes they would be approached by cattle, who appeared menacing but were only curious. Sometimes skin and clothing would be torn getting through the gaps in hedges but mostly, tried and tested routes would be followed. When they arrived home, their mother would not be pleased to see them, as it was often nearly three hours before tea time. They would have to promise not to do the same the next day but often, they did.

After the ploughing and harrowing and the making of the drills, the job would be to bring the 'dung' to the field. This normally took place in April and the three boys were nominated for the task. The first thing to be done on Saturday morning was to head to the local big farm and commission the retired Shire horse, Paddy. The large, old horse was the last of a team of similar horses who once were a large part of Burton's farm. He was still a useful animal, even though he was nearing the end of his days. James Burton encouraged the Noonans to work the horse and Bill O'Dwyer used him every summer to draw in his haycocks.

Catching Paddy was a job in itself as he was never eager to work, having had at least a week's relaxation in the paddock. He would see the boys coming with the halter and duly take off in a half trot to the other side of the field. The boys would follow and when they were closing in, off he would go again until he decided to let them catch him. Then one of the boys would lead him, slowly plodding along, to the shed by the barn where the cart was kept. The boys would then put on his harness and yoke him to the cart and away they would go to their own house.

Paddy trundled along the road to Noonan's while Sean held the reins. It was quite tricky lining up the cart with the gate and, once through, Sean drove it to the haggart, turned it around and came to a stop beside the dung heap. This was a smelly heap of cow shite, matured over the winter and ready for the field. Occasionally, the contents of the 'dry toilet' were deposited in this heap by some lazy sod who was supposed to bury it in the ground. When it was thrown into the drill in the field, the smell could be overwhelming and drew remarks from Sean's uncle Bill like 'dirty bastards'.

Once the cart was loaded up, the boys headed for the field. Paddy would take his time and plod along. In the field, the dung was deposited in heaps along the drills, ready to be spread out later. When the day's work was done, Sean drove the empty cart towards the big farm. Much more skill was required for this task, as Paddy would sense that he was on his way home and almost break into a gallop. He would have to be restrained with the reins and when he saw the main gates, he made a dash for them. The cart would just about make it through the gates and the piers bore the scars of many a close call. Then Paddy headed straight for the shed. The lads jumped down and they backed the cart into the shed. Care had to be taken to remove the harness in the correct order as, to remove one item too soon resulted in the horse sensing freedom. He would make a bolt into the yard and away to his comfort zone of a paddock filled with delicious succulent grass. This could result in serious injury, or (God forbid!) death, to one of the boys. There was not much health and safety then for three boys under sixteen!

Sean and his brothers were expected to work in the field for most of the summer. The potatoes had to be planted in early May then 'landed' a few weeks later. Sean's father sorted the potatoes the previous autumn into those for eating and those for keeping as seeds for the next season. The eating potatoes were stored in a pit made in the garden. This pit was about a foot or so deep and the potatoes were spread on a bed of straw. More straw was strewn over them before they were covered in earth. The vegetables, including turnips and mangolds, kept very well in this pit through the winter, through frost and snow, wind and rain. Sean would be sent out on a cold winter's morning to fetch potatoes for dinner, only to be startled by a rat scurrying away, having filled himself from the store. Rats, mercifully, damaged little of the precious vegetables but they had to be watched.

After the turnips, mangolds, etc. were all thinned, they had to be hoed. The weeds continued to give the plants a good run for the earth and often streaked ahead. The flies continued to torment the workers and the showers often interrupted their tasks, which was not always unwelcome!

Early July was the time when the weather had to be watched. On the first sunny day, Jim Burke would be asked to cut the meadow with his trusty mowing machine attached to his equally trusty Ferguson tractor. The old tractor ran on TVO, which was a type of paraffin and was cheaper than petrol. In the morning, the cold engine had to be switched to a petrol gravity feed, after the carburettor was drained of any TVO. Jim's Ferguson no longer had a starter motor so the starting handle had to be employed. Care had to be taken in case the engine 'kicked', which could result in a broken thumb or even an arm. When the engine eventually fired, it was allowed to warm up before it could be switched over to TVO. Turning over too early resulted in a deal of spluttering, back-firing or the engine dying.

Jim was a master at mowing and would soon have the meadow lying low. Now the weather watching became serious, as the grass had to dry thoroughly. Sean's father worried a great deal about saving his hay and visited the field frequently on his bike. When the new grass had dried sufficiently and it was time to have it turned, the old Ferguson was borrowed from Jim and Dave would drive it with the turner. Sean longed for the day when he would be allowed to drive it but for now, he was barely trusted with the horse and cart. Sometimes, there would be an unwelcome shower during or after the turning and the process would have to be performed all over again.

1961 was not a very dry year and the hay had to be tackled several times before the cocks were ready to be made. Pat Noonan was not the most patient of men and much swearing took place during the process. He expected his sons to be always available when the time was right to perform a certain part of the process. If they were not, he would rant and rave, and complain about his 'good for nothing' family and 'ham-fisted' individuals. At last, the cocks were made with the help of the family and good neighbours.

One such neighbour was John Sheridan, the postman who had Noonan's house on his daily route. He was a jolly man and always seemed to be in good humour. Sean would often listen out for his happy voice if he was waiting for a special letter or, maybe a treat he had ordered by post. This was usually a model car, such as a Mini or Austin Cambridge that he collected. John would shout out, "Another car for Sean." Not much customer privacy then!

John Sheridan could be slightly annoying whilst haymaking, as he considered himself an expert cock constructor. He enjoyed standing back and supervising the work, pointing out mistakes to the boys, who were not always appreciative of his remarks:

"That cock is not straight."

"Make that base wider."

"You'll never make a farmer."

Reply: "Thank you John," followed by a whispered "now fuck off and do some work yourself."

During the haymaking season, the neighbours would help each other out, mainly due to the uncertainty of the Irish weather. A dry period instigated a frenzy of activity in the fields, especially during the week. Young lads would hurry home from work, have a quick tea and head for the fields. Work would go on into the late evening and the workers would have the pleasure of quenching their thirst with tea from a bucket or, if they were lucky, a coldish bottle of Guinness stout. Missus Sweeney would always bring out a bucket of sweet tea and some delicious ham and cheese sandwiches, or sometimes, even a bucket of fried eggs. The good lady was a trifle deaf and once she asked one of the men if he wanted more. He said no and covered the mug with his hand. She continued to pour and the poor man screamed and ran off, nursing a scalded hand.

Sean would always remember one late haymaking evening, sipping his tea whilst leaning on his fork, tired but really appreciating the sight of the red setting sun, moving slowly behind the chestnut trees as it sank in the west.

WWI Veterans

In the summer evenings, Sean, Peader and Andy would join some of the local boys to play football. Bill O'Dwyer allowed the boys to use a rough football pitch in his field beside Brennan's house. Tom and his son, Jack Brennan, lived in one of the four cottages that was across the road from Noonan's. Tom was a veteran of the First World War, including the battle of the Somme. His wife had died some years before. His son was unmarried and he worked as a van driver in the town. They both enjoyed a few pints of Guinness and the house was not well kept. Sean and his brothers were a bit afraid of Tom, who was tall and wore a black hat and a dark long overcoat for work. The lads would peer at him through the tall yew trees and wonder what he was about.

Tom had suffered a great deal in the Great War but the local people didn't understand that. During the war, the reality of what went on at the front was hidden from the public and newspapers were censored. Reporters were not allowed to report the truth, for fear of discouraging recruits and upsetting parents and loved ones at home. Tom didn't go to Mass and therefore, he was under suspicion. He worked as a labourer in one of the local large estates. After work, he often went to the town for a few drinks and came home quite late. In wet weather, he wore a sack around his shoulders and when he arrived at a tavern, he ordered a pint and sat beside the open fire. Soon, steam would rise from the wet sack but he never seemed to catch cold or suffer any serious illness. That horrible war had toughened him up. Many of his comrades died in it, not only from battle but also from exposure to the harsh frosts and snow in the trenches, during those never-ending cruel winters in France and Belgium. The fact that he fought for Britain did not endear him to his Irish neighbours and he seldom spoke about his experiences. Tom and young men like him, volunteered to fight in the Great War, in which they were encouraged by some Irish politicians and church leaders. Like their British counterparts, many young Irishmen went to war because they sought adventure and escape from the drudgery of life in the early twentieth century; and some enlisted to get three meals a day. However, they would have never realised what they would face and that many would never return. At that time, it was said that the war would be over by Christmas 1914.

When Tom over-indulged in the public house he sometimes relived some of his worst nightmares. He talked about things like finding a dead German with new boots and when he tried to pull one off, the corpse's leg came with it. Another time, he was dodging through a field and came across a make-shift cemetery. There were half-buried bodies in the mud and he noticed a soldier's head lying on its own; the body was nowhere to be seen. The trenches were filthy places, where rats were plentiful and on 'no-mans-land', swarms of black beetles feasted on the dead and flies tormented all and sundry. Men suffered from 'trench-foot', from standing in filthy mud and water and some unfortunates contracted 'trench-fever' from the ever-present lice, which passed bacteria into the bloodstream. These men had to be hospitalised. Trench-fever could recur for the rest of one's life, in a similar fashion to malaria but not as deadly. Another nightmare was of witnessing the spectre of green poison gas, which came wafting from the German side towards his position. Men scrambled for their masks, some succeeded in getting them on, others died tearing at their clothes, desperately trying to breathe. Local people would never understand what he had gone through.

Another veteran of The Great War also lived close by. Eoin Dillon was the father of May and Annie. He was nicknamed 'Housheen' and he was, by trade, a water-diviner. He had been wounded in France and had a bullet inside his chest, near his heart, to the day he died. His war was shorter than Tom Brennan's but, nevertheless, he saw action and many horrific scenes too.

He had joined the Royal Dublin Fusiliers in 1915: the same regiment as his now neighbour, Tom Brennan. He was wounded in the chest, at the battle of the Somme, in July the next year. When he arrived at the front with his regiment, they were told that the battle was nearly over, as the German trenches had been bombarded for a week at the end of June. Little did they know that the Germans were biding their time, thirty feet below ground, waiting for the bombardment to stop!

He slept little that first night, due both to the coolness of the weather and the fear of what was to come. His battalion entered the wet and muddy trench in the early morning. Rats could be seen scurrying for safety to where dead bodies lay, half buried in the mud. The troops waited for the dawn and finally, the order came to go 'over the top'.

Eoin climbed up and over with his comrades. There seemed to be calm for a while but soon, his fear became terror as the German machine guns rattled into life, strafing 'no man's land'. There was a rifle crack and the man beside him was shot through the head, dying instantly. Almost at the same time, Eoin felt a sharp pain in his chest. He stumbled, fell to the ground and crawled along, not sure where he was or what he was doing. The German machine guns mowed down the brave men as they stumbled towards them. Eoin passed out and lay on the ground as the battle raged around him; he was there for several hours.

He felt a gentle hand stroke his cheek and he heard a soft Dublin accent call to him.

"Wake up soldier, can you hear me?"

Eoin opened his eyes. The incessant noise of battle continued; his chest hurt. Finally, he focused on a young priest, with kind eyes and a tired face, looking down on him. Father Willie Doyle SJ prayed over him and called for help. Medical orderlies rescued

Eoin from 'no man's land' and carried him to the Regimental Aid Post. Father Doyle walked with him, holding his hand and comforting him with words of hope and encouragement. Eoin could not remember this but, as he lay on his stretcher, waiting for the medical team to see to him, the good priest gave him the Last Sacrament. When he was fully awake, Father Willie asked if he would like to make his Confession. Eoin was delighted and felt at peace again. He never forgot Father Willie.

After treatment at the Casualty Clearing Station, he was transported back to a Manchester hospital, where he was operated on in an attempt to remove the bullet. The surgeon deemed it too dangerous to do so and it remained in his chest to the day he died. His war was over and he returned to Ireland but not to a hero's welcome. In fact, his English comrades who also returned to their homes after the war were not given the hero's welcome they deserved either. CS Lewis later wrote that, "he was not the first or the last soldier of the Great War to feel that the promised 'land fit for heroes' had been little more than a sham and that the years 1914-1918 had been wasted". However, in Ireland, Field-Marshall Sir John French (Lord Lieutenant and Governor General of Ireland from 1919 to 1922), published a Memorial book - beautifully illustrated by the Irish artist Harry Clarke - listing 49,000 Irish soldiers who died in the First World War. The names are listed alphabetically in eight leather bound volumes, stored in a small cabinet, which would later be on permanent display in the In Flanders Fields Museum in Ypres, Belgium.

Eoin Dillon's encounter with Father Willie strengthened his faltering faith, which he kept for the rest of his life. Father Willie Doyle SJ was blown to pieces whilst dragging a wounded man to safety during the battle of Passchendaele in 1917; his remains were never found. He made a huge impression on all he met and gave his all to comfort those who fought in the horrors of the

Great War. He wrote to his father at the beginning of the war the following:

> *"I want you to know what I went through by volunteering for the Front. God made me feel with absolute certainty – I suppose to increase the merit of the offering – that I shall be killed. The struggle was hard, for I did not want to die; not indeed that I am afraid of death, but the thought that I could never again do more for God or suffer for Him in Heaven made the sacrifice too bitter for words."*

Father Willie was definitely a one-off: a very saintly man. He was fondly remembered by many, Catholic and non-Catholic alike, for his courage and determination. He was awarded the Military Cross for bravery but many said he deserved the higher honour of the Victoria Cross. Some said that the fact that he was Irish, Catholic and a Jesuit may have influenced the final decision.

Eoin Dillon was a successful diviner and there was much demand for wells near and far. Sometimes, when he was not sure if he could detect water below, he requested a shot of whiskey to sharpen his senses. There were times when his senses became over sharpened and he had to return home. Housheen was a great character and enjoyed a drink or two. He was often seen passing along the road in later years, supported by crutches and playing the old soldier to the full (which he was entitled to do and few appreciated what he had gone through). He injured his leg one night when he supped his fill in Pitt's and took the bus to the bridge. The night was particularly dark and, after de-boarding the vehicle, he misread the road and walked into the canal. He quickly jumped out, injuring his leg on the stone edge and found his way home, not much amused and soaked to the skin. Luckily, there was a good fire going at home and he quickly removed the wet clothes and wrapped a heavy blanket around himself.

"What happened you, Daddy?" asked his daughter Annie.

"Some young pup crept up behind me and pushed me into the canal," he lied.

"The little bugger; did you know him?"

"No, couldn't see him in the dark."

Housheen was fond of little ditties, one of which went:

How many parts in a fart?
Nine! Thunder, wonder, music,
Peace, aise and comfort, wind, air and stink.

He was also known to sing old war songs. A favourite was remembered by his friends and neighbours as "Inky dinky parlez vous", a Tom Lacey song from 1915, popular with the British and Irish Forces in France. However, this was the 'clean' version, the forces usually sang: "Hinky dinky parlez vous" (or Mademoiselle from Armentieres) which could be as bawdy as the trench in which it was sung, the soldiers adding their own words, depending on how frustrated and fed up with the war they were. Of course, the number one song of the times was Ivor Novello's *Keep the Home Fires Burning*, made even more popular by John McCormack's recording of it. Sean and his brothers enjoyed Eoin's little sing-songs; not knowing what the songs were about.

The Old Soldier

He marches along the dark road,
His trench coat swinging wide,
Marching on through the dark,
Imaginary rifle by his side.

He hears a truck approaching,
Lights shining through the night,
The last of the 'Crossly Tenders'
He thinks he could be right.

He sees the German faces
Stare at him through the hedge.
Now he's in that dreaded trench,
Crawling towards the very edge.

He hears the shells exploding:
In his head it never ends.
The screams, the shouts, the moans:
It's driving him round the bend.

He went to France in 'fifteen
That small nations might exist.
Then 'sixteen saw the Rising,
John Bull's monster in the mist.

He suffered much after that;
Paddy had made a stand.
He fought on to the bitter end;
He'd hope they'd understand.

No crowds awaited his return
To a land in disarray.
A new war now greeted him:
Black and Tans and the IRA.

The porter eased the ceaseless pain
He suffers night and day.
The memories of that terrible war
Will never go away.

People point the finger now,
'There goes the soldier of old'.
He's never been seen in the church
But his story he has never told.

    – Liam Nevin

Tom Brennan came back from the war to no hero's welcome either. He had no physical injury but his mind had been damaged; his head had been messed with. The Ireland they left four years before had changed considerably. The old order had changed. The 'Big Houses' were rapidly in decline and the Easter Rising, with the disastrous executions of the leaders, had taken place. The IRA was busy making the country ungovernable and the infamous 'Black and Tans' were soon to arrive to restore order. Ironically, these soldiers, in half-police and half-army uniforms (hence the name), had been the comrades of both Tom and Eoin in the Great War and now they were the enemy.

Tom Brennan and his friend and neighbour, Paddy Butler, were, one evening, cycling desperately from the town to make the curfew but, to their horror, they heard a military Crossley Tender coming up the road behind them. They knew the tans were on patrol and soon, they realised that they would not make it to their homes. They decided to jump into a ditch, bringing with them their bicycles, which they hid in the nettles. The tender came slowly along the road. The vehicle stopped where the two terrified men hid, holding their breaths. Tom thought about the long difficult years he spent in the trenches in France and Belgium, possibly with these same soldiers, and wondered if this was the end. The veterans unbuttoned their khaki trousers and proceeded to relieve themselves into the ditch, on top of the shivering occupants, who were now more than relieved when the truck moved off again.

However, the 'Tans' were not all ex-British soldiers nor were they prisoners released for the task. Many were actually Irish and some were mere recruits from the London area desperate for a job.

Football

The Noonan boys enjoyed playing football in Bill O'Dwyer's field. The 'pitch' had a set of Gaelic goalposts, made from rough wood at one end while the other end had to make do with coats or jerseys. Sean imagined the two small hills at each side of the pitch to be Croke Park stands: one side, the Hogan and the other, the Cusack.

The games often centred on the goalposts when Noel Farrell, who was quite tall and older than the boys, volunteered to be the goalkeeper. Sometimes Jack Brennan would join in a game. He was heading for forty and a bit overweight, a smoker and drinker. In his day he played for the town team and was not a bad player. Now he could not move that quick but could certainly kick the ball. If Noel was not the keeper, some of the younger boys would do a runner if they saw him lining up a shot, as to try to stop it would be little short of suicide. Games sometimes became rough and some violence would ensue but, that is what the boys saw at the local inter-town matches and especially, the seven-aside tournaments.

An inter-county match in the big GAA field in the town was the source of great excitement. The boys would look forward to it for weeks and finally, Sunday evening would arrive and off they went with their father on their bikes. There would be a large crowd and cars would be parked all over the place. Pat Noonan and the boys parked their bikes near the ground, usually just laid on the grass verge. There was no need to lock them as few were ever stolen and if they were, they would be found somewhere else in the town.

They joined the throng on their way to the pitch. Some sported their team's colours by hats or rosettes, which, on this occasion, were either Kildare or Meath. Sellers of these items were positioned near the big iron gates, which had GAA in golden letters written over the top. There was big rivalry between the teams as the counties bordered each other. The men smoked cigarettes or pipes, filling the air with tobacco smoke as they chatted to friends and neighbours. The local brass and reed band, Saint Mary's, could be heard warming up as the family entered the ground. Sean was thrilled. It was a wonderful, warm, fine June evening and the sun was still high in the sky.

The Brass and Reed Band played the National Anthem, the ball was thrown in and the match began. Kildare scored the first point but Meath came back quickly and equalised. Big Pa Connolly, from Clane, was full-back for Kildare and played very well defending the goal. The Maguire brothers from Kilcock also played very well. The game progressed with not much in it and, at half-time, Meath was ahead by two points. At half-time, the spectators were allowed on to the pitch. The county players remained at centre field, drinking water and eating oranges while the boys and girls milled around them, seeking out their favourite football stars and trying to speak to them. The county players were mostly huge men; very tall and broad, and stinking of sweat. Sean longed to be as big as them when he grew up.

During the break the band played melodies such as, *Come back to Erin*, *The Irish Emigrant* and *Erin go Bragh*. The hawkers from Dublin sold their wares, calling out 'apples, pears and bananas' and 'the last of the Carberry chocolate' as they passed by and among the spectators. They said it was the last of the chocolate but underneath some tissue paper, many more bars were hidden: a sales ploy which often worked. Some of the boys and young – and even older men – played around the goals, kicking balls over the bar and flattening each other in the square. A good time was had by all!

The second half started and Kildare's forward, Pat Dunny, dashed from centre field and scored a brilliant goal. The crowd went wild. Meath fought back well but Kildare scored another point and all looked good. Meath got a break and Ollie Shanly scored a goal, bringing the scores to within two points. The tension mounted and a Meath and a Kildare player were sent off, as they had started a punch up, into which, many joined. The excitement grew and tempers flared. Hard shoulders were given and sneaky punches were landed when the referee wasn't looking. The crowd saw the dirty play and screamed at the referee to open his 'fuken' eyes and other, more obscene expressions. However, Sean howled with delight when the referee blew the final whistle and Kildare had won.

As the sun slowly sank behind the trees and the sky lit up in crimson gold, the crowd continued to leave the ground, chattering excitedly as they moved slowly out the gate. The different parts and events of the match were discussed and argued about in great detail. Many of the men headed back into the town for further discussions in the bars, which were already filling up.

During one game of hurling in Bill's field, one of the neighbours, Francis Monaghan, slipped on some cow dung, causing his legs to part violently and he finished up doing an untidy 'splits'. He screamed in agony and was not able to get up. The boys played on but had to abandon the game due to the howls from the injured player. Sean ran home to get help. His father wasn't in but his Uncle Ned was visiting. He came over to the field to see the injured party. He assessed his injury and concluded his diagnosis with the words, "Get up ye bledy eejit, there's nothing the matter with ye."

However, another neighbour finally bundled Francis into his car and took him to the doctor. He was diagnosed with a fractured femur and was sent to a hospital in Dublin for treatment.

The boys loved football and hurling and the long summer evenings were heaven to them. They played relentlessly, until the bats appeared and twilight descended on the field and they could no longer see the ball or each other. Then they trooped home to find their mother was preparing 'supper', which consisted of slices of bread and jam and a mug of cocoa.

Saturday evenings were bath evenings for the Noonan children. Mammy heated water for the tin bath, which had been brought in from the shed and placed in front of the roaring fire. She would lay out fresh nightclothes for the three boys. In the winter, each boy wanted to have the first bath. It would be the cleanest and the hottest, and it meant being the first to get the hot mug of cocoa and the slice of bread with delicious homemade blackcurrant jam. However, in the summer, things were different. Usually, if it was not raining, the boys played football until as late as possible but, if they got the call from Mammy, they would have to abandon the game and go in for the night. Sean was as reluctant as the others to go home first but, when he was chosen, the rewards were great: a loving mother to bathe him and serve him that scrumptious supper. Later in life, Sean would equate this experience with the end of his life. He believed God would one day call him but, although he was reluctant to go, he hoped the rewards in the next life would be infinitely greater than in this one.

Priesthood

Sean's eldest brother, Tom, was studying for the priesthood in Dalgan Park with the Columban Missionary Fathers. Dalgan Park trained young men to be priests, who would eventually be sent away to some far off place on the missions, such as the Philippines, China, Peru or Brazil.

Tom had wanted to be a priest from an early age and was much encouraged in this by his parents. They longed for a priest in the family and longed for the day Tom would say Mass for them in the local chapel. Because his parents were poor, there was no hope of getting him into Clonliffe or Maynooth, so they had to make do with a missionary society. Some less scrupulous parents sent their sons to this type of society and, when they had attained their Leaving Certificate, they pulled them out. However, the missionary societies accepted this and there were usually enough students left to fill their needs on the missionary fields.

Tom came home at Christmas and the summer and helped with the chores on the little farm. He was expected to go to morning Mass every day and to wear a black suit with a white shirt and a black tie. He willingly attended daily Mass, as it was now part of his life and he loved to take part in the commemoration of Christ's last supper. That summer, he helped with the haymaking with the rest of the boys and neighbours. He worked each summer on Burton's farm, doing all the manual jobs such as cutting thistles, making hay and general farming duties. He had gone to begin his studies in the early fifties, when his younger brothers were very young. They had not even started school so, when he returned for a holiday, they didn't recognise him.

Sean often went with his father to collect Tom from the seminary. He was very impressed by Dalgan Park. It was an enormous, grey granite building with vast, spacious corridors, which appeared to be a maze and he felt he could easily get lost in them. He made sure his father was always in sight. There was a farmyard and the original country house, Dowdstown was visible behind the trees.

Pat borrowed a car from his employers in the college, often one of the professors. Sean remembers going in a fifties Morris Oxford, complete with a split windscreen, red leather seats and the almost obligatory black paintwork. The car smelt of something he didn't recognise, but he liked it. Other times, the car would be an Austin Somerset, which was a similar type of car, with the red leather seats and again the mandatory black paintwork. He liked the name 'Somerset', as it reminded him of summer, not realising that it is an English county.

The seminary was less than twenty miles away but Sean thought it a big adventure and really enjoyed sitting up in the big swanky car, enjoying the ride. His father would say things like, "There's an auld Hillman, going well", as if cars were not expected to go well, which was possibly true!

When they arrived at their destination, the forecourt of the big house was almost black with young men (wearing black suits, black ties and white shirts) milling around and chatting excitedly, waiting for their parents to arrive. Sean's father would send him to make himself known to his big brother. It was usually with some difficulty that he would finally locate Tom. They would both hurry back to the car and, without a proper break, Pat would turn the car around and head for home. Tom noticed, when he came home that first summer, that his parents acted differently towards him. They were beginning to revere him and the foundation stone of the 'pedestal' was laid.

Tom believed he had a genuine vocation. He felt a connection with Jesus through prayer. He had been an altar server and had longed to be a priest and celebrate Mass. He knew he would have difficult times and, of course, doubts would enter his head. He missed his parents and siblings desperately in his first year. He lay in bed, in the dormitory, thinking of home and the love and security of family life.

This was an all-male environment and the only women he saw were in the kitchen or cleaning. He was, after all, a seventeen-year-old growing boy and nature had a cruel way of making him think of the opposite sex. However, he prayed to God that he could overcome these desires and fought his 'bad thoughts', which he confessed on Saturday evenings. His confessor encouraged him to look forward to travelling overseas and bringing the word of God to pagan people, instructing them in all the aspects of the Catholic Church. He read about missionary work in the *Far East*, the *Africa* and the *Advocate* before he went away.

He often wondered about some of his classmates at college, as some didn't exactly display future 'priestly' characteristics. Others seemed to have an unhealthy interest in fellow students. Sex was not a subject discussed at home or at college and homosexuality was practically unheard of. Sex was completely taboo in the Ireland of the fifties: it was considered unclean and sinful. However, most students were focussed on their task ahead and had genuine vocations, in the view of the college superiors. Candidates for the priesthood were expected to accept celibacy as part of the job, so not much time was spent on the subject during training.

Tom saw some of his old classmates when he came home on holiday. They worked as farm labourers mostly but many of his former classmates had emigrated. They had received a very basic education and some could barely read and write. The Irish education system of the nineteen-forties and fifties was certainly basic but it provided a sound foundation in the three 'R's': reading, (w)riting and (a)rithmetic.

There was little work for school-leavers in their native land. Many went to England and Scotland, destined to work on building sites, farms and building the new motorways. Some of the luckier ones made it to the USA, if they had family there who would vouch for them and give them lodgings. They had to be tough and leaving home was often difficult. Some would never return. Many would become alcoholics and destitute but very few would make it big in their new countries.

Life in Dalgan Park was well regulated. The students wore a long black soutane and on special occasions, they wore a biretta. On a typical day, they rose at 6.55am to the sound of a bell. Morning prayers were at 7.20, and a Community Mass began at 7.50. After breakfast, the first of four classes was at 9.35. Dinner was served at 1.15pm followed by a recreation period. Spiritual reading and study was from 3.15 to 5.30. The reciting of the Rosary and Benediction brought the students to tea time at 6.00pm. Further periods of recreation and study followed, ending with supper at 10.00, night prayers at 10.15 and lights out at 11.00pm. Study consisted of religious subjects, including Sacred Scripture and Church history, Canon Law and the obligatory Latin.

There was a farm in the college but the students were not expected to work there. However, they did help out around the house and the grounds. They worked on clearing the woods and they helped dig an outdoor swimming pool, which was fed by the River Boyne. Each student was expected to clean their own rooms and generally keep the college clean and tidy.

Social activities formed an important part of life in the seminary. Students played a lot of sport, including hurling, Gaelic football, soccer, rugby and basketball. An annual sports day was held in which the students competed in athletics. They produced plays and musicals but they played both male and female parts: mixing with the opposite sex was not encouraged. When they went to the cinema, they were encouraged to discuss the film but not the heroine. It was a struggle for some of the boys not to have contact with females, other than kitchen/cleaning staff and some would not be able to complete their studies because of this.

The students did have other outings to local areas, such as Newgrange and the River Boyne. In fine weather, they brought sausages and bread and cooked them on an open fire, as a forerunner to the bar-be-que.

Religion in the Irish Family

The Noonan family was very religious and much centred on prayers and church activities. The Rosary was said every night and the Angelus twice a day. Pat would give out the Rosary and all were expected to join in, kneeling at a turned-around chair and using their beads. Each child was given a decade to say; Sean usually said the third one. Father went through the litany of saints and ended with beautiful names such as 'Ark of the Covenant', 'House of Gold', 'Refuge of Sinners' and 'Comforter of the Afflicted' for names in praise of Mary, the Blessed Mother of God.

When the younger children were put to bed early, they were required to join in from the bedroom. Sean's younger brother, Andy, used to make his siblings laugh by responding with different words. For instance, 'Our Lord open my lips' became, 'Lord lope my lips' and the end of the Our Father 'deliver us from evil, amen' became 'nurse a meal, amen'. Some merriment was also initiated by the kitten playing with a dangling beads, encouraged by brother Mick, or someone breaking wind somewhat noisily, which could again be the bold Mick. He would be watching the clock while the prayers went on, as he would have a date or something in the town and his mind would not be on higher things.

Pat and Kate, together with their daughter Rose and their three younger sons would attend 'devotions' on a Sunday evening in the church. This consisted of the Rosary, followed by Benediction. They also attended the 'Perpetual Novena of Devotion' on a Monday night. This consisted of the Rosary and many prayers, including Benediction. Father Duffy sometimes got the hump when the congregation was small and would sulk, saying the

Rosary in a low voice and generally behaving like a twelve-year-old.

Sean longed to sing in the choir on Sunday nights. He took a sneaky glance at the singers from his pew from time to time. His mother told him it was a sin to turn around in the church, so a full turn was not on the cards; he chanced one eye! He believed he knew all the words of the hymns even though they were in Latin. When the hymns were sung, he sang away in his own words and thought himself ready to join the group in the gallery. He was very disappointed when he was told that he had to be fourteen to be admitted. The Headmaster, Mr Wallace, was a gifted musician and singer and usually played the organ on Sunday night. The boys who were in his class were disappointed when they heard him play, as that meant he would definitely be at school the next morning.

Lent was observed to the letter. Before Vatican II, there was no meat allowed on Fridays and several other days, such as Ash Wednesday. Rules for meals were one main meal and two smaller ones, and a dispensation would have to be obtained by a workingman who needed more food, including meat. Dances were not allowed in the local hall, by order of the parish priest and no films were shown at this time. Everyone in the Noonan household was expected to give up something for Lent. Sugar in tea, sweets or cigarettes were considered to be suitable treats to be abstained from. Sean and his brothers, together with his two sisters, Rose and Mary, would give up sweets and they would keep any they happened to be given in a biscuit tin under the bed. Mary would sometimes be unable to resist the temptation and resorted to licking a few and putting them back in the tin.

There were the sodalities every month, one for men and one for women. Banners would be erected at the end of several benches in the chapel and the members would belong to one of the guilds. There were prayers on Friday evening, followed by confessions on Saturday and Holy Communion at first Mass on Sunday morning.

Confessions were interesting, since the parish priest, Father William O'Brien, was well into his sixties and a trifle deaf. When the hatch was slid open he would hold his hearing aid to the mesh and the confession was told. However, sometimes he would miss something and say loudly, "You what?" much to the annoyance of the penitent, who would have to raise his voice and repeat his sin. Fellow penitents would hear this and wait, smirking smugly, for the poor sod to come out. However, some would chicken out and head over to the other side, to Father John Duffy, the curate, who was a younger man and not too interested in what he heard. The penance he nearly always gave was three 'Hail Marys', with maybe an 'Our Father' thrown in.

Father Duffy had a dog, which he walked a number of times a day. He would be seen walking up Main Street with the red setter and was often disgusted to see the local drunks staggering out of a licensed premises and heading for the next. He enjoyed horse riding and was badly injured once, when he fell off and suffered a head injury. A replacement curate took over his duties for a few months, who was also not too difficult to make one's confession to.

Sean sometimes went to Father O'Brien. He waited patiently in the pew for his turn. He went over and over the list of sins he would tell the good priest. Soon, too soon, his turn came to enter the confession box. The box consisted of a middle area, which had a curtain, in which the priest sat. Each side was a door to the 'penitents' box and confessions were heard in turn. Sean waited anxiously for the Confessor to finish with the person in the other confessional. He went through the list of sins he had prepared in his mind. Disobedience, lies and using bad language were usually at the top of the list, while anything a bit more serious was left till last. Having 'bad thoughts' was another sin often used. He would hear Father O'Brien say, his 'trademark' words, "You WHAT!" which made him want to dash out the door and go to Father Duffy. Then he heard the opposite hatch slide close and his opened.

"Bless me father for I have sinned, it's two weeks since my last confession," Sean began and then continued with his carefully prepared list:

"I was disobedient, I told lies, I cursed," and then the clanger, "I did 'dirty' things alone."

Well, Father O'Brien honed in on this one and proceeded in questioning the young boy:

"Did you touch yourself?"

"Yes Father."

"Did you have bad thoughts?"

"Yes Father."

The parish priest continued grilling Sean on the points of Canon Law: whether he had received Holy Communion while in grave sin since his last confession. Father O'Brien gave stiffer penances than his curate did: it could be a decade of the Rosary, or five Our Fathers and five Hail Marys.

Sean felt very clean and happy after going to Confession on a Saturday evening, despite the grilling. Cycling home along the country road, he felt at one with the Lord and he got a glimpse of, perhaps what heaven would be like. He had a great fear of going to Hell for 'all eternity' and the thoughts of eternity in that horrible place sometimes kept him awake at night. It was a great deterrent to committing mortal sin. Soon however, he would be back to reality and the temptations again, but he would make sure he received Holy Communion the following morning and feel one with the Lord. These childhood experiences were, perhaps, the very best he would ever have in his life.

There was also school Confession once a month. All the boys were marched to the church, usually by the Headmaster, Mr Wallace. A strict watch was kept on them as some tended to hide somewhere in or near the church and miss the Confession. John O'Hagen was an expert at giving the teacher the slip and often disappeared up the choir stairs, should the door be found unlocked. Other times he sneaked around the side of the church, where he enjoyed a cigarette butt, which had been carefully concealed in the top pocket of his jacket. As well as Sacrament dodging, the Headmaster was equally vigilant in ensuring that there was no chattering in the church. Anyone caught misbehaving would face retribution later in the Headmaster's classroom. Sean disliked these Confessions as he felt that they were too regimented and lacked sincerity. Sometimes, more nervous boys, if they had to wait too long, were prone to pee in the confessional. It wasn't very pleasant to close the door behind oneself to the stench of stale pee.

Before Vatican II, most Catholics only received Holy Communion once a month. In Sean's town it was given at first Mass (8.30) and not the second (11.30), as the rule was 'fast from midnight and have the right intention'.

The Altar Server

In time, Sean decided that he wanted to be an altar server. He asked permission of the PP, Father O'Brien, who was delighted. There were a few candidates, so classes were organised for after school. The pupils were given cards, with the Latin written on them. Latin seemed a strange language to the boys: there was no way they could understand it, so they had to learn it parrot-fashion ...

Priest: 'Introibo ad altare Dei' (I will go to the altar of God).

The response: 'Ad Deum, qui laetificat juvemtutem meam' (to God the joy of my youth).

The boys had to go over the words time and time again, without having a clue as to what they meant. They also had to learn the priest's words so that they did not answer with the wrong response. After learning the words, they had to learn the 'actions': change the books from one side of the altar to the other at the right time; bring up the cruets at the right time; lift the priest's vestments at the consecration and ring the bell at the right times; put up the altar cloths; put down the altar cloths. Timing was very important and to do something too early or too late earned a good telling off in the sacristy. Holding the paten under the communicants' chins, trying hard not to whack their Adam's apples, was a skilful task indeed.

Father O'Brien was very strict with his altar boys. They had to wear a surplice and soutane and black runners. The wearing of brown or dirty shoes was never acceptable. Their hands had to be spotlessly clean and no dirt under the nails. Hair had to be suitably oiled and parted. No looking around was permitted on the altar, or searching the congregation for your friends and relatives.

At last, the first morning to serve Mass came. It was a Sunday morning; the second Mass at eleven thirty. There were ten boys, including Sean, on that first morning. All were immaculately dressed with new or (mostly) second-hand church clothes. Many of their mothers and fathers were present in the congregation. Sean's mother, two sisters and a brother were there. His Mam was proud as punch.

They all sat on the women's side of the nave, the right side, whilst the men sat on the left. The church also had two transepts. The right hand one was for the shopkeepers and small farmers. It was known as the 'swanky' side whilst the left, the 'rale swanky' side, was almost exclusively for the 'big' farmers and even richer landowners, the solicitor and the doctor. Father O'Brien was known to have removed less wealthy children from the 'rale swanky' side and deposit them in the nave.

Out came the boys, led by two older, experienced servers holding a crucifix on a pole. The choir started the first hymn. The sun shone through the stained-glass windows. All was wonderful and Sean felt proud and happy. He thought then that he would love to be a priest. How the congregation would admire him and respect him when he would say his first Mass. His mother and father and all the family would be there. Heaven would be a certainty for him. How God would reward him for his wonderful life!

It was a requirement to serve Mass on some mornings before school. There would not be many in the church, just a few regular 'Holy Joes'. Sean and his brothers were expected to visit the church on their way to and from school, since it stood nearby on the same road. When Sean served Mass during the week, he usually did so with a friend. His favourite was Charlie Farrelly. Charlie would sometimes let off a fart and this would cause both boys to break into a fit of laughing. Other silly things would also cause the boys to laugh, like a funny cough or sneeze from the congregation and trying to suppress the laugh was a big problem for them both. If Father O'Brien copped them laughing, a stern telling off would follow Mass in the sacristy. The good priest never heard the farts, due to his deafness but he certainly smelt them.

One of the big 'highlights' of Sean's altar serving career came later on, when the Archbishop of Dublin, the famous (or notorious depending on one's view of him) Doctor John Charles McQuaid came to administer the sacrament of Confirmation. The servers had to go through practice sessions a few weeks in advance. The boys and girls making their Confirmation also had to do a practice in the church. The candidates had to learn their catechism by heart as the good Archbishop might ask them a question. Father O'Brien always seemed a bit tense when his boss came to his church. The Archbishop's reputation went before him.

On the big day, Sean was a bit nervous, as were the other boys. They were introduced to Doctor McQuaid in the sacristy and each boy went to kiss his ring. He was a larger than life man, with a large belly and pudgy hands. He wore his bright bishop's clothes and chatted quite freely with Father O'Brien. To Sean he appeared quite a pleasant person. Doctor McQuaid never addressed his priests other than 'father', even in private.

Sean's job was to hold the sacred book up to the Archbishop while the candidates queued up to receive the sacrament. Sean's hand trembled before the great man and he worried that he would be scolded. Father O'Brien introduced each child in Latin and the Archbishop concluded the conferring with a gentle slap to each child's cheek. The boys and girls feared this somewhat, since the older children hyped it up, saying that they would be given a good whack.

Sean's brother, Andy, received Confirmation that day. Afterwards, Andy, in his new, short-trousered suit, red tie and rosette, visited each neighbour in turn, in the hope of getting a few bob. He did get some but not as much as he expected. The treat for the day was a trip on the bus to Dublin, with Mammy and his two brothers, to visit his aunt Mary. This experience was usually very boring for the children, as Mammy and her sister spent the time gossiping and reminiscing. However, relief from this could be obtained by going for a walk with the cousins around Inchicore.

Visitors to Ireland

1961 was designated a 'Patrician year' in Ireland, commemorating the coming of St Patrick in 461. The Pope sent his blessings through his Papal Legate, Cardinal Agagianian, who took part in many celebrations that June. There was a spectacular reception for the Cardinal at Dublin Airport on 17 June, when he arrived in the Aer Lingus flagship: a Boeing 720 named *Naomh Padraig*. He was greeted by Archbishop McQuaid and the Taoiseach, Sean Lemass.

The following days were filled with receptions and formal blessings. Sean and his classmates had the privilege of seeing the holy man pass down the main street of Maynooth, in an open black limousine, accompanied by the Archbishop, on their way to the college. Crowds lined the street, waving flags and cheering. The schoolchildren had the day off, which delighted them far more than seeing the great men. Sean was not sure who this person was but his father told him that he was a 'Prince of the Church' and was worthy of much reverence and respect. The pinnacle of the celebrations took place on 25th June, with a Pontifical Mass at Croke Park.

June that year also saw the visit of an 'earthly' Prince and Princess to Ireland. Prince Rainier and Princess Grace of Monaco came on both an official visit and a private holiday. Ireland went wild for the Irish-American princess and film star, Grace Kelly, whose family came from Mayo. Sean saw the photos in the newspapers but was not lucky enough to see the royal couple in person.

It was a great time for Ireland and for Irish-Americans, as the year before had seen the election of President John Fitzgerald

Kennedy, with his inauguration in January 1961. Sean's mother and father were delighted, as was almost every household in the country. Everyone wondered if the great man would visit the land of his ancestors during his presidency. Ireland saw him as an 'Irish/Catholic' president, whereas JFK referred to himself as an American president who happened to be a Catholic. However, the new president was unique in that he was the first Catholic to hold the office but not the first of Irish descent. Andrew Jackson's parents were born in Ireland and the fathers of James Buchanan and Chester A. Arthur were Irish-born. The difference was that these presidents were Protestants. Almost all American Presidents were WASPs, that is, White Anglo Saxon Protestants, so Kennedy was certainly a mould breaker.

Missioners

The Missioners came to the church every other year and they would spend a week with the men, another with the women and a third with the children. It took place in the early summer and it was an event in itself. Stalls were erected to sell holy pictures, scapulars, statues, beads and much more. Scapulars brought a promise of never having to experience eternal hell fire to those who wore them. They were worn around the neck and contained prayers in pouches at the end.

When it was their week the children were expected to attend a 'session' in the morning on the way to school. The Missioners themselves were often weird men. No one seemed to know where they came from, or where they were going. Some were funny and cracked jokes but others told of the 'fire of hell' and an eternity there.

Sean enjoyed some of the sermons but, he feared hell so much that it gave him nightmares. Thinking of eternity also frightened him and spending forever suffering the fires of hell scared the living daylights out of him. He made sure to buy a scapular as a kind of insurance. He feared committing sin, especially those of the 'flesh'. He wasn't sure what all these sins were but, when puberty approached, the stirrings in his body worried him. He felt a need to go to confession nearly every week, in case he dropped dead and went straight to hell. What a thought!

Sean served the missions as an altar-boy. The evening session began with the Rosary and then came the sermon for the men, women or the children, depending which week it was. The servers were sent to the sacristy when it was the men's or women's week and Sean often wondered what the sermons would be about, especially the women's. What dark secrets would be revealed about adult life during these sermons? These he tried desperately to imagine but failed miserably. Adults seemed to know everything and they appeared to be confident about everything. He longed to be finished school and be a working adult.

Brian Farrell was worried about Tom Brennan's immortal soul. Tom hadn't been to Mass or Confession for many, many years. What would happen when the time came to meet his Maker? The priests told everyone that to die in mortal sin meant a certain eternity in Hell. Brian had to do something soon. Tom was getting on in years and he could get the 'call' any day; the same as everyone else really.

In the morning, Tom went over to Noonan's and called, "What time is it Kay?"

Kate would tell him the time.

Kate told Tom, one morning, of the death of a well-known man in the town and Tom remarked, "You have to be always ready Kay!"

Once, when the Missioners were in town, Brian attended one of their sermons. He spoke of Hell and the suffering of damned souls there. The priest went into detail of eternal pain and torment, causing many of the congregation's hair to stand up on their necks. Brian was one of them. Then, the Missioner added that those who did not try to save a soul might also be damned. This played on Brian's mind when he thought of Tom Brennan. He decided, there and then, that he would do his very best to get him to go to Confession. He approached him in one of the locals and explained about the sermon he had heard. After a few more pints, Tom agreed he would go to Confession that Saturday.

Brian called to Tom's house on Saturday morning at about 11.45. There was no answer. Eventually Tom's son, Jack, appeared, very drowsy and smelling of booze.

"Dad's not in," he said. "I think he headed for the town some time ago."

Brian thought that that was a good sign and hopped on his bike and headed there too. He went up to the chapel and saw that Confessions were about to start, but there was no sign of Tom. He hopped back on his bike and headed back down the town. He went straight to John Pitt's public house and there, parting a Guinness with his nose, was Tom, quite happy.

"Lave that there," says Brian "and come with me to Confession."

"Confession, Confession! What Confession? I can't go now. The priest will smell drink off me breath!" replied Tom.

"I'll be there next week," he relented.

Next week never came and Brian, though disappointed, was now happy in the thought that he had tried to save a soul and maybe his own as well.

Father William

Father William O'Brien stared out of the window of his study and didn't notice the beautiful sunset between the far-off trees. He didn't see the rays of the sun light up the clouds with a scarlet glow and the promise of a good day tomorrow in the slow setting sun: red sun at night, shepherd's delight! He had been over six years in this parish and he contemplated his future as a priest in the changing world. The world he grew up in was black and white, with very little grey.

Unacceptable behaviour, such as out of wedlock pregnancies, were dealt with by sending the unfortunate girls to institutions: notably the Magdalene Laundries. The past decade of the fifties had been very black and white indeed. The clergy were respected and never challenged. He would soon be forty years serving God and his beloved Church and he did not regret becoming a priest in any respect.

His life was largely very happy but not always easy. He loved his God and he served Him well. He grew up in County Dublin, in a family of five: three boys and two girls. His father was quite wealthy and was a senior civil servant in the city. He and his mother expected and very much hoped, that one of their sons would become a priest. The young William was a willing candidate. He loved to go to the Mass and to serve it. He admired the parish priest and longed for the day he would be ordained.

This came about in 1924, in Dublin, following six years of study at Clonliffe College. Archbishop Edward Byrne ordained him in St Mary's Pro-Cathedral in Dublin City. His family were very proud on that day. As a newly ordained priest, he was appointed chaplain to the army in Baldonnell, which he found a challenge. Some of the men were a bit rough and not very interested in religion. He then spent years being a curate in different parishes within the Dublin diocese. Father William was very pleased when, at last, he received his appointment as parish priest to his present parish.

As a young man, the 'urges of the flesh' and the 'inclinations of nature' often troubled him. His years of training in Clonliffe helped him to focus on his life dedicated to God but often, the lovely young ladies attending Mass were a big distraction. They disturbed him a bit. He was in the world and yet not in the world; this was a priest's vocation. The young ladies would, sometimes, attempt to flirt with the young handsome curate, perhaps he was their 'forbidden fruit'.

Father William was often alone in his parish house while other men enjoyed having a wife and family. However, this is what he was ordained for. These little problems would remain with him, until the last nail was driven into his coffin. He wondered about the young lads growing up in a changing Ireland. Television was now becoming popular and then there was the cinema, with all the dangers of exposing the young to sex and violence.

He was pleased that young Tom Noonan was well advanced in his studies for the priesthood. He noticed him at the morning Mass, when he was home on holidays. He was truly a good candidate and he admired his devotion to the Eucharist. He also wondered if his younger brother, Sean, might follow in his footsteps. He was a good Mass server and seemed very interested in religion. He hoped that one day, the brothers might be ordained. The Church needed young men to carry on the traditions of the 'Faith of our Fathers'.

It was a pity that young men like Tom would have to travel to a foreign country to serve the Lord as a priest: he never wanted to leave Ireland himself. Life abroad, to Father William, would be unbearably lonesome. Yes, life as a priest can be quite lonely but, he had his friends: fellow priests and family to fall back on through the years. Then again, he thought, Jesus asked that His words be taken to the ends of the earth and this is what these missionary men and women were doing.

Now he also worried about this Vatican Council, which was due to begin the next year. He loved the Latin Mass and now, there was talk about saying it in the vernacular. This is bordering on Protestantism, he thought. Don't they say a sort of Mass in English in the Church of Ireland? What will he do if the Pope agrees to implement it? He wasn't too sure about this new Pope, John XXIII: he much preferred his predecessor, Pope Pius XII, the old conservative! No way would he have allowed the Latin Mass to be abolished! After all, the valuable traditions of the Holy Roman Catholic Church had to be respected, upheld and passed on. Traditional Catholic religion was very dear to the Irish people and now, this was being threatened and it worried the good priest very much. He had taken a vow of obedience at ordination and now, this very sacred vow might soon be tested.

Father William was indeed a conservative. He loved all the rituals and ceremonies of the Roman Catholic Church. In the Latin Mass, he loved the first and last gospels, the prayers for the dead and for the souls that 'wandered the earth', the *De Profundis*, (that beautiful prayer said at the end of Mass). He loved the High Mass even more: especially the Gregorian chant, the incense and all the other rituals. He also liked the rosary and the Forty Hours Devotion weekend in October, when the students and priests from the college would come to his church to sing and chant.

The Corpus Christi feast day was celebrated on the Thursday after Trinity Sunday, which was sixty days after Easter. Father William loved this too. It was a 'moveable' feast and usually occurred in May or June. Following Mass in the church, the priest donned special vestments and solemnly taking the Blessed Sacrament from the tabernacle, headed the 'Procession' from there to the convent at the other end of the town. A more senior altar boy held a canopy over the priest to ensure maximum respect. All were expected to take part in the procession, past the mill and around the corner up Main Street, passing pubs and shops, and entering the convent grounds through the main gates. The street was lined by devout citizens: men, women and children. Even those supping beer and porter in the bars removed their hats and caps to pay homage to the Real Presence.

The traffic was relatively light in the sixties however, the Gardaí ensured the procession passed without hindrance and some of the long distance truck drivers were often not too pleased with the delay. The Rosary was said in the convent grounds and then the procession returned to the church for Benediction.

Sean was a server on many occasions and his eyes often stung with the over use of incense produced by over enthusiastic swinging of the thurible by some even more enthusiastic server. He also enjoyed these ceremonies: they were all part of the Christian life of the parish. These were also the universal rituals and ceremonies of a Church that had steadily become out of step with the changing world of the sixties. Congregations did not generally participate in the Mass. Those who could afford to buy missals, followed the celebration in them but the poorer people said their own prayers, including the Rosary, while Mass was read. They preferred to leave the ceremonies to the educated priests.

The old Pope, John XXIII, had realised that the church could not progress in the old form and had to change. The Catholic Church, before the Council, was bordering on the pharisaic. There was much concern about rituals, such as how many times a priest should walk around the altar. The human condition was over-simplified. There was no room for discussion and argument and debate were not encouraged. What the Church elders decreed went without question. Priests who objected or did not toe the line were silenced. Some were even de-frocked. There was much opposition to the Vatican Council from the Roman Curia but the future saint pressed on. He was never to live to see his vision materialise but his successor, Paul VI, continued his dream and the long awaited 'Second Reformation' became a reality: too late for many priests and nuns but better late than never. Pope John wanted to open a little window, to get some fresh air into the Church but a gale blew through, bringing much needed change of attitudes and thinking, without which, the old Church would have, perhaps, ground to a halt.

Father William's archbishop was the larger than life Doctor John Charles McQuaid, a Cavan man who had studied in the local Jesuit college of Clongowes. Father William followed his instructions every Lent and forbade dances and picture-showing in his parish. The good archbishop was somewhat feared by his priests. Father O'Brien was a fan of his and liked the way he ruled with an iron fist. He was the personification of the ultra-conservative!

The Unionists in Northern Ireland suggested that the Irish Government did not rule the Republic from Dublin, but the bishops of the Catholic Church did so from Maynooth College. Father William did not have much time for the Protestant community. The local Church of Ireland place of worship was close to the Catholic Seminary gates and the parson lived in a house up the street. He communicated with him as seldom as possible. He knew the Vatican Council would be discussing this as well.

"They should come to us and ask forgiveness, we should not go to them," he thought.

"They 'erred' in the first place, should we be going to them?"

The majority of the population of the Irish republic were Catholics and this was secured by the partition of the island in 1921. The six counties of Ulster, with a majority of Unionist Protestants, separated from the twenty-six counties of the Free State and remained part of the British Empire. Father O'Brien did not worry too much on this score.

Father William always wore his priestly clothes: a long black cassock with a cape-like item around his shoulders. Black shoes were obligatory, as was the biretta, which he wore at the beginning and end of the Mass (it was the server's job to take it from him and to give it back at the end of Mass).

Father O'Brien's Mass was not very popular in the parish, as he was slow and meticulous. He read every word of the Latin and his sermons were often long and full of fire and brimstone. He often insisted on giving the sermon at the 11.30 Mass that his curate was saying, which was a bit of a slap in the face for the younger priest. Father William normally said the first Mass at 8.30 on Sundays and was often greeted by groans and fits of coughing. The coughing got so bad at times, that the good priest would stop his sermon and wait for it to abate. The ornate pulpit, from which the sermons were delivered, was placed about quarter way down the church from the altar area, making it ideal in the days before electric amplification systems.

Another peculiar practice was to read from the pulpit the list of contributors and non-contributors to the various dues. Dues were collected in envelopes at Easter, Harvest Time and Christmas, to provide finance for the running of the parish and to contribute to the upkeep of the clergy. The contributor was required to write his or her name and address on the envelope and the amount given. The list was read out at Mass, giving the details of each occupant from street to street and townland to townland. For example: 'Doctor O'Malley, Dublin Road, five pounds; Patrick Noonan, Ballygoran, five shillings; Sean Wilson, College Road, nothing ...'

How embarrassing was that! How shameful it was for the householder and his family to be read out with a zero contribution.

The parish priest had his own housekeeper, as did his curate who, incidentally, lived in a large, separate house about a half a mile away. The fact that the parish priest and the curate had separate, substantial houses was often a bit of a scandal to the local people, especially those who lived in bad housing with large families and who could not afford the church tax or 'dues'. This was an example

Brightening Over Dillon's

of the inconsistency of the Catholic Church at the time and its apparent conflict with the teachings of Christ.

Mortality

The three boys, Sean, Andy and Peader were playing a game of Cowboys and Indians around the house and the sheds on an August bank holiday Monday, when several old Tiger Moths flew overhead. Sean noticed one in particular, flying very low and it seemed to be heading for the house. He could see the two pilots quite clearly as the plane made a left turn towards the field, running parallel to the house. The engine appeared to be idling and the propeller windmilling slowly. It continued towards the middle of the field and then, suddenly, it shot upwards and then, spinning rapidly, with the sun reflecting from its double wings, plunged into the field.

The boys could not believe what they had seen. They called to their father, who was doing some gardening but he had already seen the crash. He jumped over the fence and headed straight for the smouldering plane. The trainee pilot, seated in the front, appeared to be dead when he arrived at the scene. The second pilot, the instructor, was conscious and waving his arms madly for help. His legs were trapped in the wreckage. Blood poured from a head wound.

Pat returned to his tool shed for a crow bar and levered the dead man out first. There was some considerable risk, as fuel dropped from the tank in the overhead wing onto the hot engine. The conscious pilot was getting very concerned by this point, however, Jim Burke arrived at the scene and managed to get him out. One of his ankles was broken. Pat laid out the dead man on the grass and covered him with a coat. Just then, the heavens opened and the smouldering engine ceased to be a risk.

Sean's sister, Mary, assisted the injured pilot and then ran through the woods to the big house, which was the only one which possessed a telephone. Mrs Kelly misunderstood and thought that Mary herself was injured, as she had blood on her clothing. Mary finally convinced her there was an accident and she phoned for a doctor and a priest. When she got back to the scene, she found quite a crowd had now gathered and after a short time, both the doctor and the curate arrived. The young man was certainly dead but the instructor was moved, unceremoniously, in a wheelbarrow to a waiting car and taken to hospital.

The good priest saw the boys sheltering in the shed and remarked, "I suppose you all want to be pilots now."

Sean thought that he might. Next morning the Irish Air Corps came and removed the wreckage.

The accident was quite traumatic to Sean and his brothers. They had never been so close to a death before. Thankfully, their father would not let them see the body and ushered them to the garden to resume their play. Sean had put a small part of the broken propeller into his pocket, as a sort of souvenir. He also kept it to prove to his classmates that he had actually witnessed an air accident.

However, the next morning, the report of the accident appeared on the front pages of the *Irish Independent*. Sean and his brothers were virtual celebrities that day at school. Questions were asked about the crash and the dead man: "Did they actually see him die?" "Was he screaming?" "Was there loads of blood?"

The next weekend, the planes flew over again but they were looked upon differently. Annie and May Dillon came running from their house, screaming, when they heard the first one fly over. They were traumatised but this was a condition not understood at that time. Pat Noonan and some other neighbours thought them to be just 'silly old spinsters'.

Sean thought deeply about death. It was something he had not really thought about before. He remembered, in May, when one of his neighbours had died of a heart attack whilst working, digging up a street in the neighbouring town. This was also a jolt to the young boy. His parents always considered the dead and wondered if they were in a 'state of grace' when they passed on. Prayers were said daily for the dead in the Noonan household. They needed lots of prayers in order that they would move swiftly from Purgatory to Heaven.

It was a tradition in Ireland that, when someone passed on, a wake was held, usually on the night of the day of death. The nurse or neighbouring women would lay out the deceased, washing the body and blocking orifices etc. and dressing them in a brown habit. Rosary beads would be placed in the hands and a holy picture placed on the breast. The curtains were drawn and candles were lit. People would then come to pay their respects and join the wake in the kitchen or living room. The rosary would be recited several times. Much porter and whiskey would be consumed, together with sandwiches and cake. This would last the whole night and, in earlier days, much merriment, including singing and dancing, would take place.

Sean's first wake was that of a neighbour, who lived about a mile away. George Bolger was in his seventies when he passed away. Pat took Sean and his brother Andy to the wake. They entered the small, dark house, which was filled with people dressed in black or dark clothes crowding the front room, drinking and talking in low voices.

Sean and his brother were led to the room where old George was laid out. It was even darker, with a lone candle lit by the bedside. There was a sickly/sweet smell in the room. Sean and Andy felt terrified and did not want to approach the bed. The corpse looked very pale and wax-like. Its nostrils seemed to be flared and the eyes tightly closed. The boys were encouraged to touch it and bless themselves but both refused the touching bit and they made their way out of the room with indecent haste. Their father was handed a bottle of stout and a sandwich and the boys some red lemonade and cake. This they enjoyed but they could not get the image of that horrible corpse out of their mind, and had nightmares when they went to bed. They had known George Bolger for many years but this thing lying in the bed was not him. It was some horrible, wax-like creature, which did not even look human anymore.

One of Sean's duties as an altar boy was to serve funerals. There were often five or ten shillings to be had, as well as a break from lessons. Funerals took place in the mornings, after a ten or eleven o'clock Mass. The evening before, the body was taken into the church as the bell tolled; a very morbid time for all. The coffin was placed on supports in a small area at the back of the church while the mourners, friends, neighbours and inquisitive townsfolk crowded into the seats. One had to be seen at a funeral to give and gain respect. It was expected!

The priest prayed over the coffin and sprinkled it with holy water. The next morning, Mass was said by the priest, who wore black vestments, as was required by Canon Law. After the service, the coffin was taken by hearse to the local cemetery, followed by the congregation. Sean did not like the burial part, it was very cold and sad. The coffin was lowered into the very deep grave. The Rosary was recited while the soil was being shovelled back in. The noise of the clay and small stones thumping on top of the coffin sent shivers up his spine. Sean did not like death!

Autumn and the Chores

In late August, the dreaded Sunday came when the priest announced, "The boys' school opens tomorrow morning at 9.30."

Sean particularly dreaded going back to school. The long summer holidays were now over and the evenings would soon be getting darker. There was the little comfort of meeting your classmates again and going into a new class with a new teacher. There would be new books to get familiar with and Sean especially liked the English poetry book. He loved to read poetry but he did not relish learning boring or obscure poems by heart. As part of homework, the teacher would tell the boys to learn three or four stanzas and the next day, they would be asked, at random, to recite one.

One of Sean's winter jobs, at home, was to take the cattle from the field, to the sheds in the evening and to return them in the morning, before school. The boys shared the chores, including cleaning out the cowshed and bringing in hay to the mangers after school. The walk to and from the field along the road was often a good opportunity for Sean to try to learn his poetry lines. Irish poetry was often the more difficult as Sean did not always understand the language. He was not sure that the teachers always understood the language either!

On the walk to and from the field, the cattle, including the calves, enjoyed the fresh grass on the roadside. Sometimes they needed encouragement to move on with the help of a 'gentle' whack of a stick. Cars were scarce and usually they slowed down or stopped in case an animal wandered across the road.

One evening, Sean had just left the field and crossed onto the slightly busier road when the local vet, in his Mercedes, came roaring around the corner. Just at that time, the older cow decided to cross the road, the vet slammed on the brakes and skidded on the damp road, slightly touching the cow's backside. He jumped from the expensive car, wearing his expensive car coat and gave Sean a mouthful.

"What the bloody hell are you doing young Noonan? I could have killed one of your cattle."

He did not mention the fact that he was driving too fast on a country road and Sean was too timid to point that out. The animals, thankfully, were unhurt, although there would have been a vet on hand if one had been needed!

Milking the cows in the field during the summer months often proved to be a challenge. Usually, Pat milked the two animals himself but sometimes, the boys were sent to do it. If one or both cows strayed into ditch or even tried to break through a hedge, they were liable to scratch their udder and teats. This is when the fun started at milking time. When the milker sat himself down on the wooden tee-shaped stool and merely touched a teat, the resulting pain caused the poor cow to lash out with a kick and send him flying across the grass, bucket and all. It was an art to get the animal to settle down again and many more kicks often ensued, together with a lashing from a shite covered tail. Milking in this sort of situation could take considerable time. Pat would return home a broken man with bruised thighs, a sore cheek, cow shite around the ear and a half empty bucket of milk.

The milk was strained through a muslin cloth into large bowls and placed on a shelf. Later, Kate would skim off the cream and place it in a smaller bowl, to be churned into butter. She had a glass churn with a wooden paddle and churning was done when there was enough cream collected. This job could take quite a time, depending on the consistency of the cream.

Sean's grandmother came to stay with the family from time to time. She liked to do the churning but once, Kate asked her mother-in-law if she was tired and could she take over. However, she was surprised when the reply came as, "and then you would get all the credit, no I'll finish it."

Kate made the butter into 'pats', adding a little salt and then it was ready to use. Not having a fridge could be a problem in the summer months and sometimes, the butter went off faster than usual. Sean never liked it when this happened but was obliged to eat it rather than offend his mother. Sean's sister, Mary, never liked the homemade butter and her mother bought her a half pound of the commercial stuff every other week. Sean longed to have some of it but it was never offered.

In late August and early September, Sean and his brothers and sister rose early on Saturday mornings to search the local fields for mushrooms. Some years they were plentiful, yet others they were not. This particular year, they were lucky and found some beautiful ones: many button mushrooms and large open or flat ones. Sean brought home his mushrooms on a stalk and proudly presented them to his mother. She was preparing breakfast for the children so she washed them and fried them with bacon, eggs and bread, all washed down with piping hot tea. What a feast they all had, including mother!

When one of the cows came into 'heat' and was 'bullen', Pat would send for the Artificial Insemination or A.I. man. He had to come as soon as possible and 'service' the animal. The cow was kept in the shed until the man would arrive with all the gear and do the job. Kate brought out a basin of warm water, some soap, a towel and showed the man where the cow was.

One November day, Sean was sent to the field to 'watch' the cow, as her time was near. When he arrived, there was no sign of the beast. Eventually he found her in a ditch lying down. There were little feet protruding from her rear end (not the best birthing position) and Sean knew her time was here. His father and older brothers were at work and the cow was in obvious distress, so he hurried over to his nearest neighbour, James Costello.

James was a modest farmer who thought of himself as a gentleman, although he hadn't the money to support the aspiration. He was never that fond of work, resulting in an underworked farm. He employed the local boys to do some work in the summer holidays, such as thinning turnips and weeding but was reluctant to pay them: making excuses such as saying that their work was not up to standard and that he would pay them 'next week'.

However, James was at home when Sean called for help with the labouring cow. He came over, assessed the situation and removed some twine from his pocket. This he tied to the calf's feet and he and Sean began to pull. The cow jumped to her feet and started to move further into the ditch. Sean and James were pulled slowly through the briars and nettles, scratching and stinging their hands in the process. At last, the calf popped out and lay motionless on the ground. James immediately massaged the animal's mouth and nose and removed any mucus. Much to their relief, the little creature burst into life. Its mother took over the post-birth cleaning up with much licking and motherly care. Pat was well pleased with the calf: it was a bull and he would be able to sell it in a year's time for much needed cash.

In the spring, the ritual of releasing the calf into the world of adult beasts took place. On one such occasion, Pat Noonan was in charge of the operation and the three boys were positioned in the yard, to ensure the young animal started its maiden voyage to pastures new. The poor calf had been kept in a dark shed from birth and when the door was opened to let it out it was practically blinded. Pat held tight to the rope but the animal had more strength than expected and bolted through the door. Down the yard he raced, with Pat clinging on for dear life, straight across the road and into the ditch. It was a blessing that no vehicles were passing.

The boys followed their father. They managed to pull the calf from the ditch and point it in the direction of the field. The 'circus' continued up the road until finally, the destination was reached and the little animal was presented to the adults, who viewed it with both suspicion and curiosity. The calf was delighted with its new-found freedom and jumped and ran around the field. At last it settled down, to the delight of Pat and his sons, who headed home.

Autumn Turns to Winter

Mr O'Duffy was the master for Fifth Class, which Sean was now entering. He was not a very strict teacher by any standards. Yes, he caned his pupils but all the teachers did that. Next year, he would have the dreaded Mr Wallace, 'affectionately' known as the Rab or the Rabbi. He was 'conferred' with this nickname when he arrived in the town to take up his job. He wore a black overcoat, a black hat and dark gloves, which led the wise guys of the town to call him after the Jewish religious leader.

Mr Wallace's pupils feared him, although he was popular with parents as he got very good exam results. He used the 'carrot and stick' method but without the carrot! He was "a great believer in the value of the cane", to quote Patrick Kavanagh. The local people respected him greatly, preferring to see the results of his teaching rather than question his methods of getting them. Whenever Mr Wallace attended Mass in the local church, he would make a point of going to Communion last and then walk slowly and solemnly back to his pew, hands joined and eyes cast to the floor; a highly respectable and pious figure!

Sean first met Mr Wallace while still in First Class in the convent. He and his brother, Andy, came to the boys' school gates to wait for their older brother, Peader, so that they would walk home together. Mr Wallace came out, wearing a blue suit and red tie with matching pocket-handkerchief. He asked who they were and chatted to them quite informally. He was a short, rounded man, balding and a little overweight. He sounded so kind and amiable, they were not sure if this could be the man all boys feared. He got into his blue Volkswagen Beetle and off he went. Peader then appeared and confirmed who he was.

Every September, Sean had an occasion to meet with the Rab, when the time came to pay for the new books. Each boy had been given a bill for them before the summer holidays and, when he tendered the money, the Headmaster would ask him how much change he expected. This was an oral arithmetic question and many got it wrong, leading to verbal abuse from the teacher along the lines of, "You will end up with the spade".

The new books gave Sean great pleasure: they were so shiny and new. They had their own sweet smell. When he got home, his mother would help him to cover them. She used the leftovers of wallpaper, saved for that very purpose. His parents sacrificed a great deal to educate their children: they could little afford the new books but they willingly came up with the money.

The English poetry book was Sean's favourite. He loved to read the poems and see who wrote them and their life period – e.g. Percy Shelley (1792–1822) whose poem, *The Cloud*, Sean loved. He was only thirty years old when he died! What was it like to live in the nineteenth century, Sean wondered: no cars, no radio, no television, no films! But was it boring? He was sure it was not. There would be lovely carriages, pulled by fine horses, beautiful sailing ships and magnificent cities. Other favourites were Wordsworth's poetry especially, "I wandered lonely as a cloud" (*The Daffodils*) and lines in Milton's *L'Allegro* that went, "mountains on whose barren breasts the labouring clouds do often rest".

The History books, which told of events of centuries past, were also sources of great interest. Sean enjoyed reading about the brave deeds that were done in the name of Mother Ireland. His great hero was Patrick Sarsfield, the first Earl of Lucan, who fought at the battle of Aughrim during the Williamite Wars and who left Ireland as one of the 'Wild Geese'. There was the story of the great Irish Chieftains, O'Neill and O'Donnell, who fought the invaders to keep their land in Ulster and who lost at the Battle of Kinsale. They also emigrated to the Continent, in an exodus known as the 'Flight of the Earls'. All this was sad but heroic stuff, which encouraged students to be proud of their country and be wary of the outsiders and settlers in the North. Then there were the old legends of the Ulster heroes: Cú Chulainn and his men.

October came and Sean was well settled into his new class. The evenings got shorter; soon it would be time to bring the cattle home from the field again, and to bring in the turnips and mangolds, to be stored over winter. The last of the potatoes would also be dug up at this time. The mangolds were used as cattle feed, as were some of the turnips. The turnips had to be snagged, which meant slicing off the tops with a large sharp knife. This was not a very pleasant job, as it was done while pulling the vegetable from the sodden and often frosty ground. The boys wore woollen gloves or old socks to keep their hands a little dry. Care had to be taken with the sharp knives. Mangolds, on the other hand, had to be wrung. This was done by twisting off the tops, otherwise the vegetable would 'bleed' and all its goodness would be wasted. The turnips and mangolds were heaped up in the field and later, they were taken to the shed and finally, stored in the outside pit.

The end of October saw the arrival of Halloween. The boys looked forward to this, the evening before the feast of All Saints Day. They planned to visit the neighbours, collecting 'nuts and apples' in the evening. They would dress up in 'home made' fancy dress costumes, usually consisting of a mask, purchased in the town and a variety of old, oversized clothes: anything to disguise their identity. However, the neighbours did not take long to guess who they were and would ask them to sing a song or recite a poem before they were given some fruit or a few sweets. Some neighbours couldn't be bothered to open the door and Andy would call out, "It's Halloween you know!"

The children would come home from school that day to a delicious dinner of 'colcannon' (mashed potato with kale and onion mixed into it). In the mash, Kate hid some coins, such as a threepence and a sixpence piece wrapped in greaseproof paper. Whoever found a coin would keep it and spend it the next day. Games such as snap apple were played after tea. This consisted of an apple hung on a string and each boy had a turn at taking a bite of it, without the use of hands. Another game was to place an apple in a basin of water and each participant had a go at taking a bite in the water. A 'Barm Brack' was served at teatime. The one who found the brass ring in it would be the first of the children to get married.

The Noonan household did not have a television set and Pat and Kate thought it a good idea not to have one, ever! They thought that it would interfere with their children's education and Pat, in particular, thought there would be a lot of nonsense from England and America coming into the house – maybe even programmes with sexual overtones! This would certainly corrupt Irish society and culture.

The new Radio Telefís Éireann opened on New Year's Eve but few households had a TV to view it on. Sean was used to radio and he imagined Irish television would merely be radio programmes made visible. Those who had a television could pick up BBC and UTV. Once a week, the younger Noonan's were invited to the Farrell's house, to watch a BBC programme. They would view a programme from five to five thirty. Sean liked *Robin Hood* with Richard Greene best. *Blue Peter* was another favourite.

Bill O'Dwyer, Josie Farrell's brother, did not show much interest in television. He would come in from milking, when the children were viewing and say something like, "I hate that thing; would you lads like to take it home?"

In unison, they would answer "Yes please!"

Once the children knocked on the door at five o'clock and there was no answer. They opened the door and walking in, they turned on the television and sat down to watch. Josie Farrell was not best pleased when she came in the back door and saw them there. Next week, they stayed away but Josie had a word with their mother and they were soon back to see their programme. Kate was a bit annoyed and promised the boys they would get their own TV. They were over the moon and could not wait to have their very own set.

Moreover, the four children were invited to the Farrell's house on New Year's Eve, to see the opening ceremony for Ireland's very own television station. There was great excitement that evening and President Éamonn de Valera gave a speech, in which he said of television that there was "in the hands of men, an instrument so powerful to influence the thoughts and actions of the multitude."

On December 8th, the feast of the Immaculate Conception, Sean and Peader started their Retreat at the Jesuit house of Rathfarnham Castle in Dublin. Along with the twenty-five other boys, they headed up to Dublin on the bus and then took another one from O'Connell Street to Rathfarnham. Sean had not been away from home before and already felt home sick whilst still on the bus. He tried to imagine what this 'castle' would be like. It was dark when they arrived but he could make out a large building (not very like a castle), with a staircase leading up to the front door and another leading back down again.

A tall priest, in a long black cassock and round collar, answered the door. He greeted the boys with a half-smile and showed them into a reception room. In this room, there was a photo of an army chaplain in full uniform with the words, 'Father Willie Doyle SJ', underneath. The Jesuits remembered this priest as a very successful presenter of Retreats, and held him up as an example to those who were now carrying out this task.

After a supper of cocoa and bread, the boys were given a short tour of their lodgings, after which, they said their evening prayers in the small chapel. The tall priest gave the tour and led the prayers. He was a relatively young man, perhaps in his early forties, with greying hair. He was not the jolliest of men and seemed very strict. Sean made up his mind not to go to him for Confession.

Soon it was time for bed and that is when the sport started. Sean's room was uncomfortably hot due to a large radiator: he had never experienced central heating before. However, he retired to bed and tried to sleep. Soon, the racket started in the corridor, with lads racing up and down and making a hell of a noise. Doors were knocked on and boys pulled from their beds. Bars of soap tied to string were lowered from windows and the occupants of the rooms below were frightened witless when they heard knocking on the window, thinking that the castle was haunted. The bedlam continued for what seemed like forever to Sean, until the tall priest appeared and let out a roar, which sent the boys scampering into their rooms. Even so, not much sleep was had that night.

At eight o'clock, the large bell at the foot of the stairs rang. Sean leaped from his bed trying to figure where he was. Peader came to his room to see if he was up. Having washed and dressed, they went to the chapel for Mass. The celebrant of this Mass was a shorter priest, Father Counihan. Sean took to him straight away, as he seemed a friendlier and kinder person. He would not mind going to confess to Father Counihan.

After Mass, the boys were directed to the dining room for breakfast. This was not the usual breakfast Sean's mother cooked. He did not like the sausages and the bacon was a bit too fatty. Lunch and dinner were not much better: Sean longed for a taste of his mother's cooking. How he took it for granted! The tall priest read from the scriptures during the meal. An instruction was given that the Retreat had now begun and talking would be forbidden for the whole day. This was difficult for many of the younger boys. These two priests, who seemed to operate the 'good cop, bad cop' routine, conducted the Retreat. Whether or not it was intentional, it appeared to work.

Sean gave the Retreat his best shot. He attended the sermons in the chapel and avoided the more talkative boys. As he walked around the lovely grounds, he closed his eyes and tried his best to pray. His concentration was broken by the sound of traffic on the 'outside' and he thought of how prisoners must feel in places like Mountjoy, and the loneliness and despair they must suffer. He went to confession and Father Counihan asked if he would like to be a priest and join the Jesuits. Sean thought he would and promised to contact Rathfarnham when he reached eighteen.

In his sermons, Father Counihan spoke of the shortness of life and the need to keep God in that life. "Prayer for the soul was as important as air for the body," he told the boys. "Years fly by so quickly," he informed them, and "at my age they jet!"

The second night at the Retreat house was less hectic than the first. The boys were tired after their sleepless night before and the fun seemed to have gone out of the situation.

Christmas

Christmas was approaching and the Noonan children were getting very excited. Kate was less enthusiastic as it meant a lot of work for her. First, the puddings had to be made. She always invited her younger sons to stir the mixture and make a wish. She then made individual puddings, wrapping them in muslin cloths and boiling them over the open fire.

Pat reared turkeys, which he sold a few weeks before the big day. He kept one for their own dinner and a few others for relatives and friends. These, he killed by wringing their necks and then, the boys had to pluck them while they were warm. Sean disliked this job, and hated to see the dead bird's eyes as he denuded the unfortunate thing. The birds were then hung along the kitchen wall, wrapped in newspaper, and left to mature. The sight of them hanging there while dinner was eaten was also a bit of a worrying experience for Sean and sometimes put him off his food.

Festive paper decorations were put up the week before Christmas, together with lots of holly sprigs. The sprigs were placed over pictures and along the mantelpiece. There was a star hung in the front window and this reminded everyone of the coming of Christ and the Star of Bethlehem. A crib was placed underneath, without the baby Jesus, who would be placed there on Christmas morning. Pat never allowed the family to have a tree, as he deemed it too pagan. Churches did not have Christmas trees either, for the same reason. Not many of Sean's friends had Christmas trees and some did not even have decorations.

Christmas was also anticipated eagerly at school. The teacher asked the boys to bring in a toy on the last day before the holidays.

These would be placed in a box and each boy would draw one out. Of course, all the toys were used, some very used indeed! Sean would bring one in and he wondered what he would take in this year. There was not a huge collection to choose from and he knew he would probably get an even worse toy on the day. However, it was the thought that counted.

Mr O'Duffy looked forward to Christmas with his boys. Coming up to the big day, he drew a Christmas scene on the blackboard. He would spend days on end creating his masterpiece and the boys were very happy to watch him, as it meant no lessons and no caning. When the 'mural' was completed, Sean thought that it was very beautiful and wished he could take a photograph of it to show to his parents.

Sean and Andy still believed in Santa Claus but Sean was beginning to have doubts. Who was this mysterious person who brought gifts on Christmas Eve? Was he Saint Nicholas coming down from Heaven with gifts from God? Or, was it a hoax (as some of his classmates made out) and it was really his parents, who bought the toys and placed them in the living room after all the children were in bed? Nevertheless, Sean and Andy wrote letters to 'Santy' and posted them off. They listed all sorts of exotic toys such as cowboy outfits with all the gear, including a pair of six-guns and a sheriff's badge, model aeroplanes that could fly and the best toy cars. They knew they would not get these, but they lived in hope.

Christmas Eve came at last and the boys grew more excited as the evening went on. They peered through the curtains into the dark night, to see if they could see any sign of Santa Claus' sleigh with its twinkling lights. The bright star lit up the window and there was a sense of calm and peace in the house. The boys went to bed early, to their mother's delight, as she could get on with all the preparations for the big dinner the next day. They hung stockings on the mantelpiece before heading to bed. Sleep would not come for ages as they tossed and turned in their beds but eventually they dropped off into the land of Nod.

Tom did not come home that Christmas, as he was in his final year of study for his ordination. Kate and Pat, especially, missed him but they were willing to make sacrifices as long as he stuck with it. Kate intended to rent a television in the New Year but she did not tell Tom, in case he was tempted to give up his studies and come home.

Sean woke up early. "Had Santy been?" he wondered. He made his way to the living room and there he beheld a magical sight. In the semi-darkness (yes, it was early), he could see presents bathed in the light of the full moon, neatly arranged and everything looked so beautiful. He rushed to find his present and opened the parcel to find a brand new *Dandy* annual. In his stocking, he found a small plastic yellow tipper truck and some Clarnico Murray caramel sweets, which looked like concrete blocks in its trailer. Andy joined him and he was delighted with his *Beano* annual and an American police car, which he found in his stocking.

Soon their mother joined the boys, she was not best pleased with the early rise but hid it well. Preparation for Mass soon began and the boys reluctantly put away their presents and headed off to church on their bikes. It was customary to attend three Masses one after the other. What with empty stomachs; 'fasting from midnight' and longing to return to their presents, the minds of many could not concentrate on the religious ceremony. The cycle home seemed endless.

Everyone looked forward to the Christmas dinner. There was turkey and ham with roast potatoes, cabbage, sprouts and carrots, all home produced except for the ham. Pat did the carving after grace was said and everyone tucked in to the feast. After dinner came the much longed for pudding, with a holly leaf placed on the top; brandy was poured over it and lit. Sean especially loved the pudding, even more than the dinner itself. The afternoon was a bit of an anti-climax as parents and older siblings dozed by the fire and the younger children played again with their toys and read their annuals.

For tea, the big Christmas cake, baked by Aunty Mary, was brought to the table. It had snow-white icing and a Santa Claus with a reindeer on top. Sean loved Christmas cake and longed for a bigger piece. After tea, things livened up again when the older brother, Mick, started a singsong with the help of a couple of bottles of Guinness. Mick spun an empty porter bottle on the table and whoever it pointed to had to sing or recite a poem. Peader, Sean and Andy were quite shy and dreaded their turn. Sister Rose, on the other hand, loved to sing and wanted to sing every time but Mick insisted that everyone had to do a party piece. Soon, however, it was time for bed and the younger boys were willing to go, as they had been up very early.

Saint Stephen's Day was cold and frosty, and the sun shone brilliantly. Sean, Andy and Peader headed up the road for a game of Cowboys and Indians in the quarry field. The trees looked beautiful in their winter wear of frosted branches and ivy leaves. When they entered the quarry field the frozen grass crunched under their wellingtons as they raced to their positions. The old quarry was an excellent setting for their games. It was filled with bushes and rocks and the boys imagined the Red Indians were watching them from behind, so they began firing at them. After they had exhausted themselves fighting fierce battles they headed home.

Mother had prepared the dinner for the 'obligatory' one o'clock, mostly consisting of reheated leftovers from the Christmas dinner and the desert was fried plum pudding.

In the afternoon, the three boys and their sister, Rose, went for a walk across the fields to the place they called the 'fox-cover'. It was an old disused trail and the remains of the ancient road was clearly visible. In the ditches were many fox holes and the old hedges now grew into trees and met overhead. Like the wood, it was a magical place and the children let their imaginations run wild, as they did in Doon na Ree. They headed home again before darkness fell and the blue sky told of a frosty night to come. Sean went to fetch the cattle, who were delighted to get home to their cosy sheds and delicious fodder.

In the evening, the Noonan family had a visit from the 'wren boys'. They were young men from the surrounding areas who donned fancy dress and visited the houses to play music, sing and make merriment. All the neighbours looked forward to their coming and gave them coins or a cake or fruit.

The First Telephone Call

All too soon, the schools opened and it was back to studying again. January proved to be a very cold month, with lots of days with frost and sunny skies. In the morning, the insides of the windows had frosty patterns and getting out of a warm bed was postponed as long as possible. The beds were covered with eiderdowns with sleeves, courtesy of the FCA or CIE.

Kate always got up early. She was the alarm clock of the house. She would heat water over the fire and get the breakfast ready. Her son, Mick, got a job with CIE as a bus driver before Christmas. He was always keen on driving and drove all sorts of vehicles, vans and lorries included. He was now working in Dublin but his early shift started at 5.30am and he was not one to go to bed early. Kate would get up and call him but his reaction was not always grateful. He would lie in bed to the last minute and then dash off to work, without touching the lovely breakfast she had prepared.

One morning, Mick had a bit of a sick head and decided not to go to work. He asked Sean to call his boss from the phone box in the town. Sean had never used a phone box, or even a telephone, before. Mick said there was nothing to it. Just put in the two-pennies, dial the number and press button 'A' when your call was answered. Sean parked his bike, entered the box and was faced by the apparatus. It appeared a bit intimidating: black with silver buttons etc. He lifted the receiver, put in the two pence, pressed button 'A' when a voice answered.

"Hello," the voice said.

"Hello, hellooo," answered Sean.

"I'm, I'm, I'm," he stuttered.

"Yes, yes, what is it," said the voice, "I haven't all day!"

"Me brother, Mick, can't come to work today!"

"Mick who?"

"Sorry, Mick Noonan."

"And why not? You know we have a fuken bus service to run here!"

"Yeah, yeah, sorry; he has a bad stomach."

The CIE official slammed down the phone. Sean was shocked; he didn't fancy making another phone call for a long, long time.

After Mick had gone to work, Kate would then call her husband and the other children and they were not the most grateful persons either. One of the younger boys would have to take the cattle to the field after the milking had been done. Sean and his brothers cycled to school, all wearing the standard corduroy suit: tunic and short trousers together with a jumper, shoes and long socks (referred to as 'stockings'). Underwear was not worn until about the age of twelve or thirteen. In the wet weather, wellingtons were worn. These were kept on all day at school and could become uncomfortable. The wellingtons also rubbed against the back of the legs and this was very sore. They also encouraged chilblains!

Mick was indeed a character. He could be a 'street angel but a house devil', as his mother used to say. Yes! He was inclined to burn the candle at both ends: getting home late from a dance on a Sunday night/Monday morning then getting up early and dashing off to work, usually late. In his teens, he trained as a mechanic in the local garage and getting to work early on Mondays was a problem. He cycled like mad to work and was often greeted by Jim Leavy, a worker at Tomlinsons making his way slowly by bike to the farm, who shouted, "Short night, Mickeen?" at the struggling young teenager.

However, Mick was a very warm and kind young man and was over generous to his friends and colleagues. Many would take advantage of his good nature. He was a handsome young man and very popular with the young ladies: and the older ones too. He was a good Gaelic footballer and hurler. However, he was a bit unsettled and was inclined to switch jobs at the drop of a hat. This frustrated his father, who was quite the opposite and worked hard in the college for years on end. Mick enjoyed the local pubs, whilst his father did not frequent them. As a result, father and son did not see eye-to-eye and many arguments occurred.

Throughout the harsh winter, Peader, Sean and Andy attended school and did their chores before and after. Their sister, Rose, attended the convent, where she was in her last year in Sixth class. She had to do the chores in the house before and after school. Her mother kept a close eye on her as she was at 'that age' now.

Her older sister, Mary, was working in Dublin and went there, on the bus, five days a week and some half days on Saturdays. She worked for a dressmaker who also made liturgical vestments for the clergy. She had a boyfriend who worked in a shop in the town. Her wages were poor, as were most wages at that time. She contributed to the household budget and kept a small amount for herself. Mary had been a member of the 'Children of Mary' church group in her teens, which meant she dressed in a blue and white outfit and attended services in the church. Now, she was a member of the Legion of Mary, the adult group; Rose was now a member of the former. The nuns encouraged their girls to join up, secretly hoping that they might join their order too.

The younger siblings looked forward to a wonderful treat in January, when their parents brought them to Dublin to see a pantomime. Dad borrowed a Morris Minor from his employer, Father O'Callaghan and they all headed off to see the matinée in the Gaiety Theatre. The stars of the show were Jimmy O'Dea, Maureen Potter and David Kelly; a wonderful cast!

Dad particularly enjoyed the lovely dancing girls. Sean thought Jimmy O'Dea was very funny, although he was not sure if he was a man or a woman, as he was playing the 'Dame'. The audience howled with laughter and everyone had a wonderful time. Jimmy and David also starred in a very funny television show called *O'Dea's your man*.

Medical Men

In the winter, Sean suffered from chilblains, which could be very painful. They were caused by his feet becoming very cold and then later becoming very hot. He suffered many a night in pain, in bed, with his feet warming on a hot jar. Sometimes, his mother would heat up old irons on the fire and place them in the bed covered in a cloth. If the cloth fell off the iron, small feet could receive a nasty burn.

He also suffered, from time to time, with boils, which could be very painful. He often got a few on his neck and once, he had to go to the district nurse to have them lanced. The nurse was a middle-aged spinster and dedicated to her work. She had no time for nervous children and soon had Sean seated in her surgery, the infected area sterilised and the boils lanced with swift precision. He made his way home on his bicycle, cold and smarting from the 'surgery' but relieved it was over.

Another medical person who visited the town every Tuesday was Mr Thornton, the dental surgeon. He was a similarly built man to the local vet and they shared a non-sympathetic approach to their work. Sean regularly witnessed the vet remove quite large horns from young cattle, known as 'skulling', without anaesthetic. The poor animals roared in pain as the blood gushed from the open wounds and, upon their release from the pen, they bolted into the field. Such cruelty disturbed Sean.

Another cruel event was the docking of dogs tails. His father held the belief that all pups should only have short tails, as long tails influenced their temperament and made them aggressive. Pat placed the pup in the doorway of a shed. He tied a strip of cloth tightly at the point where the end of the tail would be, then closed the door on it. With a swift movement, he severed the tail with a sharp hedge clippers. The young pup yelped in its agony and Pat released it to nurse its painful wound, which would soon heal.

Yet another cruel practice of the time was the disposal of unwanted kittens. Pat would remove the litter from the mother cat, place them in a bag with a stone, take them to the canal and throw them in. This was not considered to be out of the ordinary, it was just what was expected to be done.

Mr Thornton, the dental surgeon, held his surgery every second Tuesday evening in the local 'hotel'. There was a large waiting room and a smaller room where he set up his chair and dental equipment, which was not excessive. There was no receptionist; patients came and simply sat in the waiting room for their turn to come.

Sean went with his mother in January. His tooth had been giving pain for several weeks, on and off. He tried to put off seeing the dentist for as long as possible. His mother sometimes got Sean to dab a painful tooth with cotton wool soaked in whiskey, which gave some relief and also tasted quite nice. In the end he had to give in and asked his mother to take him to that dreaded place.

There was quite a crowd there when he arrived. All looked suitably distressed and worried. The procedure was that the patient went to see Mr Thornton, who examined the offending tooth. The dentist did not believe in fillings. They were too expensive and time consuming and besides, the Health Board did not pay him enough, so he went for extractions.

After examining Sean, he told him the tooth had to come out. He gave him the required injection and told him to wait outside until the tooth was numb enough. The wait was distressing and Sean's imagination ran away with him, believing there would be painful torture ahead. Just then, a patient let out an unmerciful roar in the surgery and three potential patients did a runner. Even one who had already been injected. Sean felt like joining them but was persuaded by his mother to stay. When his turn came, he sat into the chair and the large dentist towered over him, with his nasty looking extractor in his hand. He swallowed hard but could not feel his tongue.

"Open wide."

"This won't hurt."

"Hold his hand, Mrs Noonan."

Sean was quite surprised when the decayed tooth was soon before his eyes and the blood ran down his throat, making him splutter.

"Rinse your mouth with this," said Mr Thornton, handing him a glass of mouth wash.

"Off you go! NEXT!"

All the way home, on his bike, Sean nursed his mouth. It began to get sore as the sedative wore off. That night, he found it difficult to sleep, as his tongue insisted on poking at the hole in his gum.

When he was in infant school, a 'travelling' dentist came once a year. He would set up his surgery in the school and extracted milk teeth as a matter of course. Much weeping occurred as the little ones went in.

Periodically, a doctor and a nurse visited the school to examine the schoolchildren. The pupils were lined up, opened their shirts and the doctor listened to their chests. Next, he placed a lollypop style stick in their mouth saying:

"Say ah."

"Ah."

"Off you pop."

Springtime

Spring arrived at last, with the beautiful wild flowers and the longer evenings. At Easter, Sean's aunt, Mary and her husband Michael came to visit from their home in Dublin. She was a very happy and jolly woman and Sean liked her very much. She always brought lovely things with her, including sweets for the children with beautiful handkerchiefs and white cotton socks for the girls.

In the afternoon, Sean, Andy, Rose and Mary went walking down the road, with Aunt Mary and their mother. They picked wild primroses from the grassy ditches and woodbine from the hedges, wild daffodils peeped through the new growth. The aroma of rejuvenating nature was uplifting and life promised to be wonderful again, after the long, dark and cold days of winter. Everyone was feeling the newness of life, as if this was the first spring. The older sisters chatted about people they knew when they were young, and the good old days gone by. They remembered how, when they were teenagers, they used to go to the dances at the crossroads and enjoyed taking part in the 'half-sets' and waltzes, dancing to music provided by a fiddler or an accordionist. The road was quiet and the sun shone brightly as they ambled along, with not a care in the world.

The party crossed into one of Kelly's fields, through an iron stile and walked across to the cemetery, in order to visit the grave where Sean's grandparents were buried. They all said a decade of the Rosary for them. It was about half a mile from the road and always a lonely place. An old, stone wall surrounded the cemetery and in the centre stood the ruins of an ancient church. Yew trees grew wild among brambles and briars and many of the graves were neglected, with their headstones either fallen or broken.

Many bodies lay beneath the ground unmarked; some lay there for many centuries perhaps even a millennium. Sean thought of the words of Thomas Gray (1716-1771), "Each in his narrow cell forever laid the rude forefathers of the hamlet sleep."

Donaghmore

The full moon creeps above the hill,
Behind the old church wall.
Her pale light spreads across the field
And o'er the gravestones fall.

I gaze across to the old walled ground,
Where my dear ones peacefully lie.
I think of many happy days
I spent with them as a boy.

I think of days of long ago,
When life was without care.
My dear folks cared so much for us,
In a house not far from here.

They lived a humble, simple life
But a life so full of care.
Each day, they worked so very hard
And ended it with a prayer.

They cared for us without a thought;
A selfless life they led
And now they lie across the field,
In their eternal bed.

They lie beneath the hallowed turf,
Facing the rising sun
And there, I wish to share their plot
When my life is finally done.

*Like the words of Thomas Gray
Whose 'Elegy' I learned and loved:
The hearth, no more for them shall burn,
From here they'll not be moved.*

*The old stones tell of gentle folk
We knew in days long past.
When life was new and we all thought
It would forever last.*

*But life is short, as now I know,
My mother often said
And we will all, so very soon,
Be laid in our eternal bed.*

*Sadly, with heavy step I go
From the road to Ballygoran,
To go away again, too far
From the home where I was born.*

*A home I loved and sadly left,
In search of Fortune fair
And now, I wish I never left
And still be living there.*

    – Liam Nevin

Sean's older sister, Mary never liked the cemetery. Earlier, in January, she got a terrible fright when she was passing the gates of the place. She came from work as usual on the bus. It was seven o'clock and very dark, save for the light of the rising moon behind a distant hill. She watched as the lighted bus pulled away, leaving her all alone in the world.

There was no sign of a car, so she made her way up the bridge and walked swiftly along the dark road. She always dreaded passing the lonely gates, with its stone, ivy-clad piers. The gates creaked in the wind and the chain holding them together rattled in sympathy. This night, she thought she heard a woman crying in the field. She thought, 'No there can't be someone in that dark field.'

She paused and listened again. Her skin prickled and the hair stood up on the back of her neck when she heard the crying resume. It was further away in the field and seemed to be moving towards the silhouette of the ancient church. She nearly wet herself and ran and ran, fearing to look back until she reached home. She hammered on the door and fell into the arms of her startled father, weeping uncontrollably. It turned out that that same night, Jim Burke's father died and it was said that the Banshee followed that family. Pat promised his daughter that he would meet her off the bus every winter evening from then on. Sean was often sent to meet her but he did not mind.

Easter was a busy time for the altar servers. They had to attend rehearsals for a few days in Holy Week. Seamus, the clerk, conducted the sessions, making sure all the procedures were followed correctly. There was Holy Thursday, with its long Mass. The practice of washing of the feet as a sign of humility had not yet come in. Good Friday had a long service in the afternoon, which seemed to go on forever. On Holy Saturday, the long service was followed by Midnight Mass, which Sean enjoyed. Fathers O'Brien and Duffy were splendid in keeping strictly to the rituals and ceremonies. A bunch of drunks arrived late at the Mass, but they did not make trouble and the Mass was soon resumed. Sean was tired and hungry when he got home and was allowed the luxury of a delicious chocolate marshmallow egg. It was after midnight, after all!

Easter was always a great time of the year, as it heralded the beginning of spring proper, giving everyone new hope and the memories of the harsh winter would soon be forgotten.

Off to Africa

One Saturday, Pat and Kate brought the younger children to Baldonnell military airfield, to see the Irish soldiers leave on their United Nations mission to the Congo. A local lad, Edward (also known as 'Jasper') Connolly was one of the men leaving that afternoon. He had worked with their older brothers, Dave and Mick, in the local garage but had decided to join up and head for foreign shores. Jasper was indeed a character: full of wit and fond of the dry joke, he enjoyed a drink and a smoke and loved to watch the football matches. His decision to volunteer to go to Africa surprised his friends, as he was thought to be well used to his comfort zone – i.e. the local boozers and the football pitch. Anyway, he had signed up for the tour and part of his decision was to save a few bob and see the world.

On Jasper's mind (whilst outwardly not giving a damn) was the tragedy which had taken place nearly two years before in the Congo! In November 1960, Baluba tribesmen had ambushed and killed nine Irish soldiers. The tribesmen only had bows and arrows. A man from one of the local towns was among the dead. However, Jasper still wanted to go and the day had now arrived. When he returned from his mission, he was given a new nickname of 'Congo' Connolly: a great honour indeed!

The large, troop-carrying Douglas Globemaster aircraft were lined up at Baldonnell. Compared with the aircraft that the children had seen before at Dublin Airport, these were enormous. Their father often brought them to Dublin as a treat and from the balcony of the lone passenger terminal, they had seen beautiful planes such as Viscounts, Fokker Friendships and DC3's but nothing the size of the Globemaster. Sean loved to see the Aer Lingus aircraft, with the green shamrock on the tail and envied the passengers filing out from the terminal and boarding them. He hoped one day he would fly on one and tried to imagine the view he would get from the large windows of the Viscount.

The troop carrier, on the other hand, had four enormous piston engines and the big American Star with the words, 'Military Air Transport Service' emblazoned on its side. Vehicles were loaded through a large double door through the nose. Troops were seated in an upper deck and it was accessed through a door at the back. It lacked the creature comforts of the aircraft at Dublin Airport but Sean still wished he could fly on one. The troops had a long flight ahead. They would stop for fuel at Cairo and another African city before landing in the Belgian Congo.

The spectators watched as the troops marched out with their kit bags and climbed the steps on to the aircraft. Mums, Dads, brothers and sisters waved their goodbyes and tears appeared in many eyes, including those of the soldiers. The doors were closed and then the huge engines roared into life, belching smoke and the occasional flame out the rear. The chocks were pulled away from the wheels and the big birds began to taxi to the runway. The planes took off, one by one and soon disappeared into the low clouds. Some of the crowd stayed behind, gazing up into the sky and worrying about their loved ones.

Farrell's Lane

The children returned to school after the short Easter break and looked forward to the coming summer. When the weather improved, they went without an overcoat but were often caught in a shower. The bus fare to school was two pence each way but the children often walked home and spent the money on an ice cream or a few sweets. They went to Murray's shop on Main Street, where they met up with their friends. One of the local characters and his brother, nicknamed Guy and the Lodger, came to the shop but were short of a penny to get an ice-pop. Guy eventually was given the penny and marched to the counter and purchased a lovely orange-flavoured one from Mrs Murray. He was delighted but on getting to the door, the ice-pop fell off the stick and he walked on it. What a disaster! However, another kind soul gave him a penny and he bought another one.

The walk home took the Noonan's across the fields. They headed up the railway bridge and turned left into Farrell's Lane. The mayflower was in bloom and its scent filled the air. A blackbird was startled and, complaining loudly, flew off in a huff. The bees were busy at the beautiful white flowers:

Farrell's Lane

Down Farrell's Lane
We wandered home
In summers long gone by.
We lolled along, without a care,
When I was just a boy.

Liam Nevin

Along the lane,
The mayflower bloomed
As we skipped lightly by,
With worries none
And pressures few,
When I was just a boy.

When school was o'er
We headed home
Along that leafy lane.
Our hearts were full
Of many joys
Before we knew of pain.

Down Farrell's Lane
We wandered home
In days I still can see.
When skies were blue,
Disappointments few
And life was full of glee.

We wandered down
That dusty lane,
I remember with a sigh.
The days were long,
Our hearts were strong,
When I was just a boy.

Down Farrell's Lane
We passed the place
We knew as Doon na Ree,
Where many a happy afternoon
We dreamed beneath the tree.

We dreamed of days
As yet to come,
We wondered how and why,
When life would be
So very strange
When I was not a boy.

Now Farrell's Lane
Has long since gone,
As now it is a street.
Now houses stand
Where the mayflower grew
The air is not as sweet.

– Liam Nevin

The children made their way along the dusty lane, which had no hard surface and grass grew down its centre. Bold briars inched their way into the lane and were beaten back by the lane users, including cars and tractors. The silence of the countryside was broken only by a passing train, which sounded its horn as it rounded the bend and approached the station. They reached the end of the lane at Farrell's farm. It was a land-commission farmhouse and quite a modest farm.

Peter Farrell was a lovely man and waved to the children as they made their way across his field, to the final field before home. However, when his crops started to appear over the ground in the spring, he asked them to not to cross the field but to use the headland. They crossed the ornate pier remains and entered Bill O'Dwyer's land. As they walked along the beaten path, they noticed their beloved pets lying patiently on the little hill they knew as the 'Hogan' stand. As soon as Rufus and Sweep saw the children, they dashed to greet them, tails wagging excitedly, enjoying every loving pat. If the children came home by bus, they would see the dogs from the road, staring towards the piers from the hill, again running madly towards them when called.

Tragically, these much-loved dogs died a year later, having been poisoned by rat poison, which some unthinking householder had left out on pieces of meat. The dogs died in agony, much to the distress of the children and especially Sean. Not even trying to force cigarette tobacco down their throats and swinging them around to make them sick worked. The animals were buried in the garden and mourned for many days. How the children loved those pets! Their father eventually got them two crossbred pups, which went a long way to ease the pain but the memory of Rufus and Sweep would always remain fond in their memories.

Confirmation

Sean made his Confirmation that year. Some of the older boys wound him up by saying that, at Confirmation, the bishop gave you a smart slap on the cheek, which hurt a lot. Sean was a bit worried about that. In the weeks before the conferring of the sacrament, about ninety per cent of the school day was spent studying catechism. The bishop could ask any question, so the teacher took no chances.

The big day finally came in June. Sean was togged out in a light blue suit with, to his disappointment, short trousers. A white shirt, a red tie and a large rosette completed his outfit. His father took his photo on his Kodak Box Brownie. Black and white of course!

It was an Auxiliary Bishop and not the great Archbishop McQuaid who administered Confirmation. The boys were directed to the 'men's' side of the church and the girls to the 'women's'. The Bishop asked Sean a question, which, luckily, he knew the answer to. (It was not 'Who made the world?') The candidates filed up to the altar and were confirmed by the bishop. The gentle 'slap' certainly did not hurt.

That afternoon, Sean went to see a film at the Carlton cinema in O'Connell Street, Dublin with his mother and siblings. The film was *The Big Country* starring Gregory Peck. They loved the brilliant music and the beautiful scenery and, of course, the 'larger than life' actors. Sean fell in love with Carol Baker, with her lovely red hair, feisty character and American accent. Afterwards, they all had chips and an ice cream in a nearby café and happily took the bus home from Aston Quay.

One of the conditions of making one's Confirmation was to 'take the pledge'. Sean had to sign a pledge to abstain from alcohol until he was twenty-one, which he did happily. He knew something of the culture of consuming alcohol in the local establishments, of which there were four on Main Street alone.

Father O'Brien lectured the boys on the subject when he visited the school. He spoke about the advertisements posted by Arthur Guinness around the town. They said that 'Guinness was good for you' and that it 'gave you strength'. The posters showed a man lifting the shafts of a cart with the horse sitting in it. There was always the toucan with his golden beak somewhere in the picture. The Priest argued that Guinness was not good for you, for many reasons, including health and finance. It led to the wide and well-trodden road to Hell. He also mentioned the dangers of the consumption of whiskey and advised the boys not to touch the spirit until at least the age of forty.

Sean listened well to the good priest, without really understanding what he meant but wondered about what he had said. He had heard his mother talking about Joe McGuire coming home from the pub 'stinking drunk' and he had smelled the bad breath of old men who had been imbibing in places such as John Pitts'. His uncles sometimes came to the house in high spirits, smelling of this bittersweet booze. When the booze began to wear off, their mood would change and the darker side crept in, and then serious arguments often ensued. The arguments never came to blows but tended to get a bit heated at times.

The Rab

"Come up Noonan you braaat!" roared the Rab.

Sean nearly crapped himself. What had he done? He jumped up and went to the teacher's desk. The Rab was holding Sean's composition copy and staring at the pages.

"What is this all about, Noonan? You were told to write four pages of the composition: there is only three."

"I thought I wrote four, Sir."

"So, you can't count now; hold out your hand."

Sean received three swift slaps with the cane, which hurt considerably. He returned to his desk, squeezing his throbbing hand under his armpit to ease the pain.

Sean had started in September in Mr Wallace's class, the Sixth: an event that he had dreaded! When he was in the junior classes, he had often heard the Rab roaring at the scholarship candidates. These were the 'brighter' boys, who had been selected for extra tuition in the hope of winning a scholarship to further education. Some regretted being selected, as it meant extra hours being 'taught' by the Rab. Two of the McInerney brothers were selected and Sean often heard them squealing loudly, when being 'corporally' punished with a cane. Their parents looked to the glory of their boys winning a scholarship and were not that concerned about the means used to obtain this end. They judged Mr Wallace by his results and his results were often very good indeed. Parents turned a blind eye to his methods, believing that a Headmaster, especially of Mr Wallace's calibre, would never harm their children, either physically or mentally. Well, not much anyway!

Mr Wallace was, as said before, a great believer in the value of the cane. He administered it liberally on a daily basis. Another form of 'torture' was the slap on the ear. This was a favourite of his and he was very quick to whack an unsuspecting victim, approaching him from behind. No harm was meant, physically or mentally!

One particular Monday morning, the Rab asked the class to place their composition copybooks on his desk. Sean had made sure that he had written the obligatory four pages. The composition was to be about an event in the town, which had to be exciting and descriptive. The spelling had to be exemplary and the writing was required to be neat and tidy, no blotting of the copybook!

The Rab selected a copy from the middle of the pile. It was a bit scruffy and some of the pages were loose. He lit a cigarette: an un-tipped Goldflake made by WD & HO Wills in Dublin. The cigarette dangled from his bottom lip and the smoke wafted upwards into his nostrils. He had warned his pupils never to smoke, yet he did so himself. After a while, the cigarette formed a tail of ash, which dangled precariously until it broke away and fell on his tie. The Rab quickly brushed it away.

Andy Green once arrived late for school and was sent to the head. He stood outside the classroom waiting for the Rab to appear, wondering what his punishment was going to be. He had a good idea! The teacher saw the boy standing there and beckoned him to enter.

"Green! You brat! Why have you been sent to me?"

"I was late for school Sir; me alarm clock didn't go off." Andy's family could not afford the luxury of an alarm clock.

"Late again, you mean, hold out your hand."

"What's that brown mark on your fingers, Green? Have you been smoking?"

"No Sir, that's rust off me bike." Andy's family could not afford the luxury of a bicycle either.

"Don't lie to me Green."

Whack, whack, whack.

"Get back to your class."

The Rab returned to his morning task, picked up the shabby copy and began reading the 'Nipper' O'Sullivan's composition.

The Runaway Horse

The gidgger reilly was yolkin jonny de horse when he broke loose and hedded up de lane pullin the kart behind him de messia nolan ran after him and cudnt catch him as he was runnin very fast

The Rab had a broad smile on his face and the Nipper began to acquire a false sense of security.

De horse galloped down de lane an de people were jumpin outada way and screamin loudly pieball doolan hopped on his bike and chaste jonny tryin to katch him

The Rab began to giggle and the pupils joined in. The Nipper was getting more confident and even allowed himself a smile. The teacher read on and the merriment continued ...

de horse dragged de kart down de mane street and gard breeny lept out near de college an katched him de horse kicked the gard on the shin an lots of lads laft loudly ...

The alliteration was lost on the Headmaster.

Suddenly, the Nipper caught a blow to his left ear, followed swiftly by one on the right.

"Spell 'the', you braaat Sullivan."

The Nipper didn't hear the question as his ears were ringing. Another blow followed and the Nipper fell to the floor whimpering. The enraged teacher continued pointing out the spelling mistakes and the appalling grammar and continued meting out the punishment. The class watched in horror as the scene unfolded and began to worry how their own compositions would fare.

The Nipper returned to his seat, trying to suppress his sobs and easing his painful hands by squeezing them under his armpits. The Rab continued his examination of the compositions and several other boys received slaps with the cane for bad grammar and spelling. Just a few desks in front of where the Nipper sat, a boy asked a question and the Rab came over to inspect the book he was reading. His back was turned towards the Nipper and one of the wise guys, closest to the Rab's arse, performed an Oscar winning mime of smelling it and making disgusted faces to his fellow students. The Nipper's sobs turned quickly to bursts of suppressed laughter, mingled with snots. The Rab turned around:

"Sullivan, what are you laughing at?"

"I saw a funny thing outside the window, Sir."

"What was it?"

"A fat pigeon fell off the windowsill," he lied

"Don't tell lies, you braaat."

And the Nipper received yet another whack across the face. It was not his day!

Monday mornings in November were cold. The sky was clear as there had been a substantial frost. Peader, Sean and Andy set off for school on their bikes. The sun was rising over the distant wood, giving the sky a deceivingly warm glow but the frost covering fields and hedges told a different story. They had woollen gloves, a hat and a warm coat but they still wore short trousers with long socks and black shoes. Sean's hands were still cold, even with the gloves and his legs were freezing. They arrived at the school and lined up at the main door. Boys arrived steadily and every now and then they glanced at the bend on the road from Dublin, which continued on its way to Galway, many miles away. They watched for a certain car: a blue Volkswagen Beetle, which was driven by the Rab. They hoped against hope that the car would not appear, as it would mean an easier day at school. To everyone's disappointment, the little German car appeared at the turn. It moved, as usual, to the back gates of the mill, where it turned and headed back to the junction and turned left towards the school. The Rab was nervous of that corner and preferred to go to the mill gate to turn.

The car pulled up at the school gates and the well clad teacher got out, sporting a trilby, a neck scarf, leather gloves with woollen insides and a thick winter overcoat. The boys shivered in the line, some wiped their noses on their sleeves or their gloves. The Rab passed a certain boy who was about to wipe a green snot with his sleeve and promptly received a whack on the ear.

"You disgusting little brat."

Several snots were swiftly sniffled up and the teacher went to open the door, saying aloud, "Dia is Muire dhuit", in Connaught Irish.

"Dia is Muire dhuit is Padhraig," came the reply in chorus, in Leinster Irish.

Sean and his friend, Seamus Timmons, were given the dubious task of collecting the lunch papers and scraps from the play area after lunch. It was a handy job in the summer and autumn when a lesson could be dodged but in the winter, like this day, the yard was cold and the wind whistled through the field and up the legs of the short trousers. However, the previous Friday, Sean and Seamus had not done their job, as it was raining heavily. The Rab called them to the front of the class and asked why the yard had not been cleaned. Their excuse was not accepted and each got three slaps on each hand. The pain was excruciating, as their hands were still cold from the cycle to school. They were sent straight out to pick up the papers in the frozen yard. Their hands still hurt and they had great difficulty picking up the items, some of which were frozen to the ground.

The Rab drank Nescafe instant coffee and ate Jacob's Kimberly biscuits while he sat on his stool, close to the warm stove. The boys looked on, feeling very hungry and longing for one of those delicious biscuits. The coffee smelt great too! Most had little to look forward to in their sandwiches: Sean and his brothers had jam in theirs. Different boys were chosen to make the coffee and select the biscuits for the teacher. When Sean's turn came, he was too afraid to steal a biscuit but it was said that others did and some even less scrupulous boys 'gobbed' in the Nescafe and swept chalk dust into it, together with any other item that would not be easily detected by Mr Wallace.

Fear of the Rab was often extreme and, even at that young age, some pupils suffered agonies from their nerves. If a teacher was absent, his class was brought to the Headmaster's and lined up around the room. One day, another class was standing and one particularly nervous student was closest to the Rab's desk. They were set to reading prose while the Rab corrected some homework. As usual, he was smoking, a cigarette dangling from his lower lip and occasionally, he wiped the falling ash from his tie.

Martin O'Donnell eyed the Rab over his tattered English prose book, wondering what he was correcting. Suddenly, the Rab lifted his hand to scratch his head and Martin threw the book into the air, scattering pages in all directions. The Rab roared with laughter but made the unfortunate pupil scramble underneath the desks for his disintegrated book.

When a class was positioned standing around the classroom, reading or learning poetry, the worst thing a pupil could hear was for the Rab to announce, "Back to back." This meant the boys would face each other and not be able to 'cog' over a shoulder or whisper an answer in a troubled ear. The Rab fired questions to each boy in turn. If an answer was not satisfactory, corporal punishment would follow. It was usually of the 'cane' variety.

On another occasion, the Rab went from the classroom. The boys were quiet for some time but there was no sign of the teacher returning and so, the usual bedlam erupted. Items were thrown around the room; lunches and bottles of milk were removed from schoolbags and hurled in every direction. Martin O'Donnell began to get confident and shouted at other pupils acting the big boy. Kevin Mannion was a brilliant mimic and could imitate the Rab's voice very well. Unknown to the boys, Mr Wallace had gone to chat with the school gardener, who visited once a month. Anyway, the Rab heard the commotion from outside the open window. As he was not the tallest man in the world, he had to stand on tiptoes to see in to the classroom. He shouted in, "O'Donnell sit down you braat."

Martin thought it was Mannion, mimicking again and shouted back, "Aah shut up ya auld bollocks!"

Then, too late, he realised his fatal mistake when he saw the bald head with the piercing brown eyes at the window. He simply sat down and awaited his fate. His punishment was soon enthusiastically delivered by the Headmaster.

Sean was daydreaming during the Irish lesson, in which the Rab read a book of short stories. Irish was always taught in 'Irish' and English words were never used. It was a story about a newspaper talking about the stories it contained. Sean's mind drifted off to a lovely summer day, making hay at home with his Dad and brothers. Suddenly the Rab shouted, "Dun na leabhair" (close the books) and Sean awoke from his daydream.

The Rab, seeing that Sean had not been listening, asked him several questions. His answers were not satisfactory and he was ordered to the front of the class and further questions were fired at him. Sean did his best to answer but failed miserably and each time, he received a slap across the face. His ears began to ring and he had difficulty hearing the questions.

To make matters worse, his brother, Andy and his class were standing by the walls, as their teacher was absent. This was very embarrassing, as he was the older brother and he felt everyone staring at him. He refused to cry and the Headmaster grew angrier by the minute and included the cane in the punishment. Eventually, Sean gave in and burst into tears and the Rab backed off. Sean returned to his desk totally humiliated and hurting both physically and mentally. His first year in the Rab's class was turning into a nightmare. He loved to learn but his fear of corporal punishment made him very unhappy.

Class discrimination was rife in the school. The doctor's son, the shopkeeper's son or a rich farmer's son were treated leniently and seldom slapped. However, these boys usually moved to a posher school later as their wealthier parents didn't want them mixing with the 'lower class' children. Some may have had doubts on Mr Wallace's teaching methods. On the other hand, the poorer parent's boys were treated with contempt and thrashed regularly. If a parent complained about their child being punished, the Rab would simply sit the child down in a corner and refuse to teach him.

One day, in the middle of a class, the door burst open. A mill worker, a tall, broad, well-built man in his late thirties, walked into the room. His clothes were covered in flour and his boots made white footprints on the floor. He walked leisurely up to the Rab and punched him firmly on the nose. The victim staggered backwards, clutching his bleeding nose and the tall man simply turned around and walked out. The teacher refused the mill worker's son any further tuition.

The Rab was perched on his stool, conducting his class, when out of the corner of his eye, he noticed Father O'Brien coming from the parish house and heading towards the school. He quickly hid the cane and continued his teaching. Soon the parish priest appeared at the classroom door. The Rab instructed the class to continue reading and went outside to greet the cleric.

The class listened for the pair to begin their conversation and soon, the classroom degenerated into chaos. Papers were tossed in the air, inkwells were thrown and pupils were ejected from their desks. The Rab swiftly opened the door shouting "QUIET PLEASE" and the noise calmed down but erupted again after a short while. Then Mr Wallace and Father O'Brien entered the room.

The boys stood up as quickly as possible given that some were out of their place. The teacher's face was red with fury and his look promised much punishment to come but he controlled his feelings very well, and the good priest addressed the class. He preached against the evils of drink and he hinted about sins of the flesh and 'company keeping' but most of this went over the boys' heads, as they were contemplating what the Rab's retribution might be. Others were curious about what those sins of the flesh might be and hoped the good priest would elaborate but, disappointingly, he failed to do so.

Father O'Brien finished his sermon and left the room. He and Mr Wallace chatted again in the corridor and the boys hoped, in vain, for a reprieve. No such thing occurred and the Rab re-entered the room in a fury. The usual suspects were lined up and received three slaps of the cane each. Then the dreaded statement was made, "You will all be kept in after school for extra lessons today."

Being 'kept in' was punishment indeed. The pupils longed for three o'clock and home time. Staying on for an extra hour was very disheartening. It was also a pain for the mothers, who had prepared the dinner for three thirty. Sean's mum was one of these, as she fried rashers, eggs and mashed potatoes, left over from the midday meal, for that time. There was then a problem of keeping the meal warm. She normally boiled some water, placed the plates on top and kept the food as warm as possible. It annoyed her but she dared not question the Headmaster. She knew that Mr Wallace was well respected in the town and if he gave his free time to further educate her boys, what could she do? Sometimes, if there was an urgent job to be done after school, such as getting the cattle tested, she would send in a note and all the boys would go home on time.

Life was not all hard work and corporal punishment however. A school excursion to the great city of Cork proved to be a great adventure for Sean and Peadar. They were very excited, as they had not travelled on a train before. The boys were collected by bus from the school early in the morning. It was a lovely summer's day and a lark sang high over the playing field as they boarded. Each boy had a sandwich and a drink. Sean and Peader had jam sandwiches and a bottle of milk each. The Rab and two other teachers accompanied the party. Mr Wallace roared at them occasionally, to remind them to behave themselves.

They arrived at Sallins station at nine o'clock and the boys filed on to the platform. Soon, the big green diesel CIE train rounded the corner and everyone cheered in their excitement. Sean climbed up into the large carriage and he and his best friend, Seamus, rushed to a seat and made themselves comfortable. The Rab came through the carriage giving more instructions: no running, no changing to another carriage and no sticking heads out the windows.

Sean loved the train. It moved so fast and he enjoyed the beautiful scenery: the large green fields, the rivers, the mountains including

Slievenamon. They travelled through the counties of Kildare, Laois, Tipperary and Limerick, and all too soon, they approached the big city of Cork. The train slowed down and Sean and Seamus couldn't resist the temptation of pushing up the window and having a look out. They were enjoying the wind in their face and through their hair when whack, whack, they both received a slap on the back of their heads. The Rab roared at them, "Get your heads in this instant you brats, what did I tell you before we left Sallins?"

The slaps nearly garrotted the two boys, who quickly sat back into their seat, clutching the back of their heads and their throats.

Cork City was wonderful. Sean had been to Dublin but Cork was something else. The River Lee sparkled in the sunlight and the gulls screamed as they fought over discarded fish thrown from the incoming trawlers. There were large merchant ships moored along the quay. They walked through the streets, stopping to buy sweets, visited the Cathedral and heard the Shandon bells. They had lunch in Woolworths and, after a very pleasant afternoon, boarded the train and headed home. Sean's father collected them from the school and they chatted all the way home about their wonderful day.

A less enjoyable excursion was the one to Belfast that took place the next year. The train stopped at the border just past Dundalk. Armed police and customs officers boarded the carriages and seemed to look suspiciously at everyone. The people in Northern Ireland (or the 'Six Counties'), had a funny accent, which the children found hard to understand. They went to City Hall with the Union Jack flying above it and Stormont Castle, where the Northern Ireland Government sat. They were impressed with its size and appearance. They could see the huge yellow cranes of the shipyard, Harland and Wolff, in the distance. They were told about the building of the Titanic in the city.

Sean thought it strange to see different police officers in the city. They were not the Garda officers he was used to in the Republic and they wore guns. Pat Noonan was not happy about his son visiting a 'foreign' country. Sean felt that they were not welcome in the city and the whole place felt very alien.

Television Arrives

The winter of 1962/63 was very cold. The temperature really plummeted in January 1963, making life very uncomfortable. Luckily, a brand new Rayburn solid fuel cooker had replaced the open fire that autumn. It gave out wonderful heat and was a real revolution in cookery. It kept the living room warm but the bedrooms could still be very cold. The hot water bottles warmed the beds and the Rayburn was very useful in heating the pots and kettles of water. The main fuel was 'coke': a cleaner by-product of coal.

Kate decided to rent a television to cheer up the family. Sean and his siblings were delighted. At last, they would be able to watch their very own TV set. One day, when they came home from school, they were thrilled to see a brand new television sitting on a shelf in the living room. They couldn't wait for the programmes to start at five o'clock. There was only one channel, Radio Telefís Éireann, but they didn't care: it was a new adventure. They watched the test card in 'glorious' black and white for the best part of twenty minutes until, at last, the programme began. The children were enthralled, as was their mother.

However, Kate had a heavy heart. After Christmas, her son Michael, (he was commonly called Mick but she preferred his proper Christian name) decided to pack his job in and head for London. Both she and her husband were devastated, as were the older children, Mary and Dave. She hadn't gotten round to writing to Tom yet: she didn't want to upset him. The younger siblings didn't realise what going to England really meant.

Many of Mick's peers had already headed across the water, to 'fuken England' as neighbour Jack Brennan referred to that country. Some returned for a holiday, sporting a Cockney or other regional accent; others never returned and a few returned after several years, in a coffin.

Kate worried about her son working on a dangerous building site, or constructing one of those new-fangled motorways. Maybe he would drive one of those big red London buses. She worried about the dangers of drinking and whether her son would lose his religion in that Protestant nation? These things she mulled over in her mind and she prayed every night that Michael would be safe, and return home to her very soon.

Dave came in from work at six o'clock the night the television arrived. His brothers and sisters were glued to the new television screen. Dave decided that the picture wasn't right: not clear enough. He proceeded to adjust the aerial, which sat on top of the box, to everyone's annoyance. He made it worse; he lost the picture and he received a considerable amount of abuse. Eventually, the picture was restored to near normal and Dave sat down to eat his dinner, still not satisfied with the picture but warned not to touch it.

Sean enjoyed all the programmes and his mother had to order him away from the TV to do his homework. Even the advertisements were entertaining: the Esso ad, featuring the 'Esso Blee Dooler' was a favourite. Kate began to wonder whether getting the television was a good idea.

The children loved *Dáithí Lacha*, a cartoon in Irish about a duck and a cat (Pusheen). Dáithí wore no trousers. Charles Mitchell read *The News*. He had a stony face that showed very little emotion. He read the news very well but just concentrated on the auto-cue and his facial expression seldom changed. Most of *The News* was merely the radio news. The newsreader was the main focal point with the occasional photo or picture of the subject and even a bit of newsreel. *The Weather* was a simple affair, with the presenter sticking symbols on the map of Ireland. *The Angelus* was rung on the television at six o'clock and everyone stopped what they were doing to pray.

Many of the programmes shown during the six hours a night that RTÉ transmitted were American. Sean would later particularly enjoy such American shows as *Green Acres*, starring Eva Gabor and the spoof spy show entitled, *Get Smart*. In *Green Acres*, there was a character named Fred Ziffel, who insisted that his name was spelt as 'zee aye effle effle'!

The Aer Lingus Boeing 720 was shown taking off at the close of transmission as the National Anthem played, making Sean hope that one day, he would fly to America on it. He was not allowed to stay up weeknights to the end but only on Fridays and Saturdays.

Pat had no interest in television, apart from watching a Gaelic football or hurling match on Sunday afternoon. Later, when the Rugby Union international matches were shown on a Saturday afternoon, he refused to watch them, as he did not consider them Irish enough, even though Ireland would be playing. He had grown up in a world without radio, never mind television and longed for the old days. He especially hated the new *Late Late Show* with Gay Byrne on a Saturday night. Kate and Mary loved it. Sometimes, he would come in from the 'tool shed', switch it off and retire to bed. Kate and Mary sat looking at the blank screen and dared not switch it on again. It was said that there was no sex in Ireland before Gay Byrne and his *Late Late Show*!

Family Life

Pat took great comfort in his little tool shed. It was his escape world where he worked on little projects, such as getting an old motorbike up and running again. He also procured old bicycles and built a good one for one of his boys by cannibalising the old ones. He always wanted to be a mechanic. As a youth in the 1920s, he came to the town to be an apprentice mechanic. He was disappointed when his father could not afford the fifty pounds to give to the garage owner and he had to make do with working as a servant in the college.

Pat had grown up in an Ireland that was rapidly changing. He was a boy when the Easter Rising took place. He listened to the older people talking about the great damage to the buildings in Dublin City and the annoyance of the local people that this disruption should take place. However, this all changed when the executions of the leaders took place and these men became heroes overnight. He remembered the War of Independence and the terrible Civil War, the violence and tragedies of which were the birth pangs of the Irish Free State or Saorstát Éireann. The Civil War set brother against brother, father against son, neighbour against neighbour. These 'differences' existed in most of the Irish Republic and were still around in the nineteen-sixties. Families were identified as either pro-treaty (Michael Collins) or anti-treaty (De Valera) by the newspaper they read: *Irish Independent* or *Irish Press*. Protestants and middle class Catholics tended to read *The Irish Times*.

In the college, Pat looked after the priests' cars, doing minor servicing and keeping them ticking over. He occasionally did a service on a neighbour's car; usually not getting paid very much for it, but he enjoyed the work. He never felt accepted in his new location and the local people named these 'blow-in' college staff as 'saucepans', as they mostly worked in the kitchen. He would always feel an outsider, even when he was over forty years in the town. He had raised a family of eight children, (nine if the stillborn baby is included). He now slept in a separate bed to Kate as she could not risk having a 'tenth' child and this was the only solution to family planning. There was no one to talk to about such matters. Good Catholics were expected to have sex only for procreational purposes and certainly not for pleasure.

Pat worked long hours in the college for little money. As a youth, work in the college meant very little free time outside of the self-contained establishment. Some of the boys 'escaped' into the town over the high wall to meet girls and to have a pint. Those days were now thankfully gone. Now he cycled to work after he had milked the cows. He came home at one o'clock to have his dinner. He would bring home porridge and dripping, wrapped in newspaper, on the back of his bike. College dripping was superior to the local butcher's dripping and was used extensively, for almost every dinner. The hot dripping left in the pan was poured over the plate, as a sort of gravy.

As well as a pipe, Pat enjoyed a cigarette and he would bring home a packet of Players Gold Leaf to Kate. In fact, Mick would smoke anything he could get his hands on. Very occasionally, he was given a fine cigar by one of the professors at work and he would keep it for a special occasion, to smoke in comfort. He would also bring home a bar of Fry's Chocolate Cream, or a 'thrupenny' bar of Cadbury's milk chocolate for Rose and Andy and Sean to share. Sean eagerly waited for him to come home, not just in case he brought some sweets but also, because he loved him and felt secure when he was in the house.

Unlike Pat, Kate enjoyed having the new television in the house and also liked listening to the radio. On her way home from Confession, on a Saturday evening, she loved to have cod and chips from the 'chipper' van parked in the square. The van served fish in batter, sausages and, of course, chips to the town's folk. She had worked as a ladies' maid in a large house when she left school. She had enjoyed the work although the pay was not very much and she had to live in. She got one day off a week and a half-day on Sunday, to attend Mass and visit her parents. Kate met Pat one Sunday on the nearby bridge, when she was out walking with her sister, Mary. He was out walking with a friend and colleague from the college. They fell in love straight away and married two years later.

Kate had a hard life, being pregnant nine times and then bringing up the little ones. She loved them dearly but the stress of taking care of them was often a big strain on her health. Her eldest daughter, Mary, was a great help to her in later years, when her last three children were very young. She often wondered why some families had only two or three children, while she had so many pregnancies. Birth control was not an option. The only way to prevent any further pregnancy was to abstain from sex. This became a strain on Kate and Pat's marriage but there was no other way out. It had to be done. There was also always a worry about money and how to pay for things. She firmly believed that if she were given one hundred pounds, her financial worries would all be gone.

Sometimes, she envied her sister, who came on holiday from Manchester with her husband, wearing the best of clothes and made up to the nines. However, she never wished to live anywhere else but Ireland, poor and all that it was. Her sister had had to go to England many years before, on the orders of her mother, as she became pregnant out of wedlock. There was no place for her at home, since she had committed the ultimate misdemeanour: having sex before marriage. Having sex outside marriage was simply not acceptable in the nineteen-thirties Ireland and even into the sixties, in some parts.

Pat and Kate grew up in a world where one had to accept the consequences of one's decisions, including the person one married. Marriage was for life and not something to be run away from when times got tough. It was a world of 'mend and make do', not 'throw away and get something else'. It was a world where ordinary folk had very little and consumerism was a word yet to be invented. Lives were simple and often hard and most accepted life as the 'Will of God'.

John Sheridan, the postman, arrived at Noonan's gate in his usual jovial mood, with an important letter for Pat and Kate.

"Hello Kate," he hollered "got your much expected letter from England."

Kate rushed out the door and grabbed the letter. "Thank you John," she said, studying the envelope to make sure it was the one she expected. It certainly was. It was from dear Michael.

She hurried inside and opened it. Michael was very well and working on a building site. He was living in digs in Shepherd's Bush in London. He was happy. He promised to come home soon, to see them all and sent his love. Tears came to Kate's eyes as she read the letter again and again. She missed her dear son so very much.

The Deaf and Dumb Man

One Good Friday morning, Kate was busy making the beds when she heard a knock on the door. She wondered who it might be at this time of the day. Neighbours usually called out, as the door was always open when the weather was fine, as it was that day. She wasn't expecting anyone who would have to knock.

She went to the door and there was a medium-sized man wearing a shabby, check-brown jacket, dark trousers, scruffy black shoes and a brown hat. He held a bundle under his arm. He handed her a note saying he was deaf and dumb and that his name was Patrick Brady. 'Oh my God,' she thought. 'This is Good Friday and maybe this is Jesus Christ Himself, in disguise.'

She showed the man to the chair by the fire. She put on the kettle and soon they were both having a cup of tea. He ate the homemade bread and butter she had given him with relish and Kate noticed that he did not possess many teeth. His unshaven chin almost met with his nose as he chewed. He wrote her several notes, explaining that he was a 'man of the road' and that he was very grateful for her hospitality. He stayed all morning and Kate was getting a little annoyed, as she had her housework to do.

The family came in and out and wondered who this strange man might be. She explained and again mentioned that maybe he was 'The Saviour' Himself. She noticed that the deaf and dumb man seemed to be a bit amused when she said it.

'But he is deaf,' she thought! 'Could he lip read?'

She dismissed the thought and continued with entertaining her guest. Eventually, Pat Brady decided to take his leave, lit a cigarette, picked up his bundle and headed off. He handed Kate yet another note, thanking her and saying that he would call to see her soon again. She was not sure if she was pleased or not.

He did come again, many times, not always at a convenient time but he was never any trouble. He came in and sat by the fire, read a newspaper and wrote his notes. He enjoyed a cup of tea and a smoke and left when he thought his welcome was wearing out. He never forgot the families that gave him shelter from the Irish winters and showed him kindness. If a member of those families passed away, he always came to the wake to pay his respects. In a way, he was a representative of Jesus Christ, who asked His followers to treat the poor and the disadvantaged as they would have treated Him.

Pat Brady served in the Second World with the British army. He had been in the Irish army during the first year of the war, which was known in Ireland as 'The Emergency'. The news came in every day on BBC radio of how the war was progressing in Europe and how the Nazis were advancing through France, towards the Channel. The Irish Government policed and maintained the country's 'neutrality' through draconian censorship, to prevent any news of the war getting through to the population. This included films and, of course, Radio Éireann. The governmental party so censored the national radio station that some dubbed it 'Radio Fianna Fáil'. The Irish people relied on the BBC and English language German radio, as newspapers were also censored. William Joyce, an Irishman, broadcast on German radio and was nicknamed 'Lord Haw-Haw' (the British hanged him in 1946 for high treason).

Hitler was planning to invade Britain and from there, Ireland would be for the taking. Pat soon realised that the Irish army was hopelessly inadequate to resist any invasion and, if Britain could not keep the Germans out of their country, Ireland had no hope. He made his way to the United Kingdom Permit Office in Dublin, got his permit to travel to Britain and enlisted in the British Army there. It is calculated that some fifty thousand citizens of the Free State enlisted up to 1945, including five thousand from the Irish army. He fought in North Africa, including the Battles of El Alamein, under the command of Field-Marshall Bernard Law Montgomery. The fighting was different to the First World War, as there were no trench stalemate situations. Although the weather was very hot and the fighting could be fierce, Pat Brady survived without physical injury but his mind was affected.

He returned to Ireland after the war and kept his head down for a while. As in the Great War, there was no hero's welcome in Ireland or, to a lesser extent, in Britain. He found it difficult to get a job. Men who left the Irish Army during 'The Emergency' were considered to have gone AWOL (absent without leave) and labelled deserters and traitors. He was questioned repeatedly about where he spent the last five or six years when he applied for a job and he could not get employment anywhere. Eventually, he had to 'take to the roads' and rely on the kindness and generosity of the country people.

Pat suffered with his nerves following his experiences in the war. He also lost his voice from time to time, when he was under stress and anxiety. He decided then to act the permanent 'dummy' and threw in deafness as well. His hearing had suffered during the war from being close to heavy guns and general battle noise, so this became his chief claim to pity and generosity whilst travelling the roads of Meath and Kildare.

Pat Brady, like Jim Murray, had his 'safe' houses. He also worked seasonally on farms and took advantage of the hay barns to have a good rest. One late summer evening, after working all day storing the last of the hay into the barn, the farmer rewarded his workers with plenty of porter, ale and whiskey. The day had been sunny and dry and the men got stuck into the fine drink. Pat had his fair share.

Later that evening, a young couple decided to avail of the same hay barn facilities to have a bit of a 'coort'. They were getting down to some serious business when they heard someone enter the barn. The intruder flung his hat in the corner and in full voice, began to sing the 'Rose of Tralee'. The couple recognised the singer as none other than the 'deaf and dumb man', Pat Brady himself. He had taken quite a lot of drink and, thinking that he was at last on his own, he had decided to sing the song. The two lovers could not believe their eyes and ears and sneaked out the back of the barn, their passion having been somewhat dampened.

A few days later, they told their friends and neighbours about the incident but no one believed them. They could not really specify where they had heard him sing, due to the circumstances, so their story fell on deaf ears.

In fact, Pat kept up his somewhat harmless pretence for many more years, until one day, he suffered a stroke. The people in whose house he was staying rushed him to hospital. Days later, Mary Noonan and her friend Noreen went to visit him in hospital. They saw him in the ward and as they approached the bed, they heard this Cavan accent coming from him and could not believe what they were hearing. Could he speak all along or had the stroke restored his voice? They could not tell.

The Irish Emigrant

Mick Noonan boarded the mail boat at Dún Laoghaire and tried to make himself comfortable. The January evening was cold, with a stiff east wind. He was already missing his family but he knew he had to go. He wanted something better than driving around Dublin in a CIE bus. He had an address of an old friend in London, who promised that the streets were indeed 'paved with gold' and that England needed help in the rebuilding of the country, after the devastation of the Second World War.

The old mail boat, *MV Maude*, made its way slowly out of the harbour as Mick stood on the deck and gazed at the lights of Dublin City until they faded from his view (as in the popular song *Rosslare Harbour*). He entered the cabin area with a heavy heart. Was he doing the right thing he asked himself? The sea became quite rough as it sailed further into the Irish Sea, so he made his way back to the rails and hung overboard to gulp the fresh, if cold, air.

Many passengers began to feel sick. Mick ventured to the toilet for a pee and had to pick his way through the vomit and the piss to the urinal. The waves lashed the side of the boat as she bobbed up and down in the angry sea. A priest held on to the same rails and gripped his missal but the wind caught it and his holy pictures and memorial cards flew away seawards. He was lucky to have been able to hold onto his holy book. Mick wondered when he would ever see Holyhead. In his queasy seasickness, he began to regret leaving his native land.

The ship docked, at last, as the wind and rain continued to pelt down. It continued to bob up and down. Mick noticed the strange

Welsh accents as he made his way down the gangway at Holyhead and suffered another few pangs of homesickness. He gathered up his tattered old suitcase and made his way to the train. It too was old, nearly as old as the mail boat. He entered the carriage and again tried to make himself as comfortable as possible. He was now tired, cold and weary, and still a little seasick. Other passengers looked as he felt and clutching their own tattered suitcases and bags, they sat there in their Sunday clothes. Some displayed labels with their names written on them, hoping to be met by an agent who would have digs and work for them. They were a sad lot, many forced to leave their homes and families, as there was no work for them in Ireland.

Mick slept on and off in his uncomfortable seat and between naps, he looked into the black night through the window and saw only his reflection staring back. The noise made by the wheels on the track seemed to call out, 'You'll never go back; you'll never go back; you'll never go back; you'll never go back!' Mick again had doubts about the wisdom of his adventure to this foreign land but the hope of making a fortune dismissed them. He was always an unsettled man, young as he was. There was always that greener field, far away that he must see and experience. There was always that pot of gold waiting for him, just over the horizon, at the end of the rainbow. He believed that one day, he would find it and he would return home with riches enough to set up his dear parents in a beautiful house, with all the modern facilities and comforts.

Now, Mick was passing through Crewe on his way to Euston. The wheels of the train still echoed that lonely refrain. He suppressed his sadness and looked forward to a new life in London. There would be craic with the lads, loads of money and there would be the girls! He thought about all those lovely, lonely Irish girls longing for a boyfriend, who, they hoped, would eventually be their husband. He was not interested in getting married but he could chat them up and maybe get lucky.

It was still dark when the train arrived at Euston in the early hours. People were already on their way to work. He noticed many 'coloured' people driving buses and working as porters, which seemed very strange, as he never saw such people in Dublin. The 'Big Smoke of London' never eased up. 'Big Smoke' was the right description, as the cold winter air was polluted with smoke from houses and factories. He got a tube train to Shepherd's Bush and made his way to the address he had been given. He saw the notices in the digs as he passed along the street, 'No blacks, no Irish, no dogs'. He knocked on the door of number 10 Askew Road. A stern lady, in an apron and rollers, opened the door and looked him up and down.

"Yes?" she said, in an Irish accent.

He was relieved.

"I'm Mick Noonan. My friend, Freddy Lafferty told me that you had a room to let."

"Ah Freddy, yes come in."

Mick was shown into a room with four beds: he was not renting a room, but a bed. He would have to share the large room. There was a communal toilet on the landing. The rent was two pounds a week, rent one week in advance. Luckily, Mick had the two pounds and handed it over. He was used to sharing a room but not with strangers. He lay down on his 'new' bed and was soon fast asleep. He dreamt of days gone by: of green fields and mother's love.

Next morning, Mick headed off to the White Hart public house in Acton, where he was to meet a big contractor about a job. He met the big man in the public bar with his two 'minders' and immediately bought him a pint. The minders refused the offer. John Delaney, a native of Mayo, looked him up and down and asked him a few questions about where he came from and where he had worked before. Mick was quite short but he was well built and used to hard work and he could look after himself. He knew something about work on the 'buildings' and John Delaney decided to give him 'the start' on a trial basis. He was told to begin work on the Monday and that he would be picked up by a van outside this pub. He was expected to have a good pair of boots and a proper warm jacket, as the weather was about to get even colder. The men shook hands and Mick left. John Delaney stayed on to consume several more pints of Guinness, which were brewed in Park Royal, not so far away in London.

The White Hart was a great Irish pub and the labourers met there to be paid on a Friday night. Music and dancing took place there every Friday, Saturday and Sunday nights. The 'craic' was mighty. The Irish bands played plenty of the old ballads, which painted a picture of Ireland as the 'Tír na nÓg', which it never was or ever would be.

Most of the men lived, like Mick, in a common room where they rented the bed only. There was no point in spending the weekend in such a room, so they congregated in the pub and spent most of their wages over the weekend. Some spent all their wages on drink and gambling and by Monday morning, they were skint. Then the ganger was approached for a 'sub' and life for them was a never-ending merry-go-round of work to pub to bed. Many would become alcoholics, ending their lives early and returning to Ireland in a box. In the words of Ralph McTell's song, "Sleeping late on Sundays, I never get to Mass; it's a long, long way from here to Clare."

Mick loved the craic in the Irish pubs and met many new friends. He drank in the Crown in Cricklewood and danced in the Galtee More. Sometimes, he ventured as far as Hammersmith and enjoyed dancing in the Palais. The various Catholic clubs, such as Quex Road in Kilburn, were also excellent places to enjoy an evening. These clubs were mostly built by the Irish community and were heavily supported by them. He loved the dancing and the girls all loved him. They waltzed and jived and danced the slow foxtrot, which gave the boys and girls an excuse to have a bit of a smooch. The work was hard but the craic was good.

He wrote home as often as he could and was homesick for many months. On clear nights, from Askew Road, Shepherds Bush he could see the Plough and the Bull in the sky, through the light pollution but it reminded him of seeing the same constellations from the yard at home. Mick was quite sensible with his money and even managed to save a little. He intended to go home at Easter but bad luck playing cards in the White Hart put paid to that. He knew his parents would be disappointed but he was determined to go home in August.

The GAA clubs were great places to find company and entertainment. Mick joined the Tir Chonaill Gaels in Greenford. He enjoyed playing all over London, particularly at Ruislip. There was a fine pitch there and the clubhouse was excellent. After a game, everyone headed to the bar. The music started — Irish and 'Country and Western', of course and the porter flowed. There were always plenty of lovely girls there, to tease and have fun with. Men from every county played with the many Gaelic Football clubs. Some even played for London in the Irish championships. The games were well supported and the Irish community got together, the same as it did at the church clubs and Irish pubs: and for a short time they were back home in the Emerald Isle and not in a land they would never call home!

Irishmen would be always 'Micks' and 'Paddys' in the United Kingdom but they found solace in their fellow countrymen. However, they made the mistake of bringing their prejudices and grudges from Ireland with them. They argued and fought each other. Mick was often caught up in a fight in a pub and sometimes took a hiding, when he was talking when he should have been listening. He could also give a hiding, as he was inclined to be argumentative, especially after taking a few drinks.

The Irish in Britain were often their own worst enemy, as they exploited each other, especially in the building trade. Sub-contractors ('subbies' to the workers) demanded 'bribes', in the form of the offerings concealed in the 'match box', or no work was given out. They also expected to be fed porter on Friday and Saturday nights, and Sunday mornings, in the 'Irish' pubs by the labourers, who in turn were expecting work on Monday morning. As said before, for many labourers, life in Britain became a never ending and often vicious circle: a roundabout they could never get off. Others managed to get off the ride and educate and better themselves, by taking advantage of the opportunities available in Britain. They would experience prejudice, which often bordered on racism but they persevered and made a good life for themselves. They married and their sons and daughters often became very British and assimilated into society. However, the second generation 'plastic' Paddys, as often as not, became as Irish as their parents. They cherished and were proud of their roots.

Whilst many of the men and women who came to Britain over the years from Ireland, looked back at the 'Old Country' through rose-tinted glasses and felt home sick, many were glad to be out of the place. In Britain, they could be free of political stalemate and religious bigotry and even oppression. They were very pleased with the work and the great pay packets which would never be forthcoming in Ireland.

Michael did not come home, as promised, that Easter, much to Pat and Kate's disappointment. They prayed for him at the services, including Midnight Mass. Kate wondered if he was safe and if he managed to go to Mass.

That Good Friday, the rain came down and Sean, Peader, Andy and Rose went into the shed for shelter and played cards. Their favourites were 'Beg My Neighbour' and 'Snap'. The rain hammered on the corrugated iron roof. They wondered if it would clear up before they all went to the Good Friday service at three o'clock. Sean and Andy were to be servers and they had rehearsed most of the week. Mammy called them in for dinner at one o'clock. They were all a bit gloomy with the wet weather. Their mother glanced out the window as they ate their dinner of fried egg and potatoes (no meat on Good Friday and fish was reserved for the adults) and said cheerfully, "It's brightening over Dillon's."

Then she added, "The cabbage and onions need weeding."

But then, remembering what day it was and that working was not an option, to the boy's great relief, she said it was a joke.

Exiles Return

The build up to John Fitzgerald Kennedy's visit to Ireland was tremendous. Everyone looked forward to the first visit of an American President to the fourteen-year-old Republic of Ireland. Hardly a news bulletin went by without a mention of it and the newspapers featured many articles about the coming event. In school, Sean and his classmates did many projects and wrote compositions on what they expected the visit to be. Ireland was going to be on the world stage, after many years of struggling in the doldrums. The teachers reminded their pupils that America was the greatest nation on earth and that a descendant of a poor emigrant from Wexford was now its President.

On Wednesday, 26 June 1963, the great man arrived in Ireland, landing in the evening at Dublin Airport, following a historic three-day visit to West Germany. The President of the United States had been warmly welcomed in Europe and was moved to anger at seeing the Berlin Wall, that symbol of Communism. He looked forward to his visit to his ancestral home in Ireland. The visit was dreamed up as a 'rest' for him, as he needed to give an excuse to Congress to make it happen. He was welcomed at Dublin Airport by Irish President, Éamonn de Valera and An Taoiseach, Sean Lemass. Both presidents were born in the USA and the older one had been sentenced to death in 1916, the year before the younger one was born.

JFK was driven in a beautiful black Chevrolet soft top, which was the car that Sean imagined driving whilst riding his bike to town. There was wide coverage of the visit to his ancestral home in Dunganstown and to the town of New Ross in County Wexford. He had been there before, in 1947, as a thirty-year-old

Congressman. He had been given the use of Lismore Castle in County Waterford, the Duke of Devonshire's 'extravagant country home'[1] as his sister, Kathleen, had been married to the Duke's eldest brother. He visited Mary Ryan's very basic and simple cottage with two of his sisters, Eunice Shriver and Jean Smith, who seemed delighted with the welcome they received. Another member of the entourage, however, Pamela Churchill Harriman (who had been married to Randolph Churchill, son of Sir Winston) was not impressed with the place.

Many relatives came to see and meet him and almost everyone in Ireland wished they were a relative too. He was a wonderful figure of a man, larger than life; or so he appeared on the television. Sean longed to see him in reality. Few people knew that he suffered greatly with back pain and sometimes resorted to using crutches and multiple painkillers, but his public face showed little of this.

He met all the dignitaries and laid a wreath at Arbour Hill, in memory of the men who were executed in 1916. This ceremony was the highlight of the President's visit. He addressed the Irish Parliament (the Dáil), in Leinster House, where he received a standing ovation. He was purposely diplomatic about the division of the island, which was then beginning to be an issue. JFK was not a total stranger to Ireland as, apart from 1947, he also visited in 1945, as a 'hack' journalist and in 1955, he came as a Senator, with his wife Jacqueline. He had a difficult time arranging his historic visit, as Europe was somewhat in turmoil, with Harold McMillan having to deal with the Profumo affair and Italy and Germany having their own difficulties. There was also the growing race issue in the United States, which needed to be addressed. However, he did make the trip and Irish people were sad to see him leave but very much hoped that he would return to the 'Auld Sod' one day soon.

---

[1] *JFK in Ireland: Four Days That Changed a President* by Ryan Tubridy. HarperCollins, 2010

One Friday evening, in early August, Dave Noonan popped into the town to get a packet of fags. He cycled back along the Dublin road and as he approached the canal bridge, he noticed the bus from Dublin pulling in and offloading a passenger. A well-dressed young man in a blue three-quarter coat with a black velvet collar, complete with 'drain-pipe' trousers and 'winkle-picker' pointy-toed shoes alighted from the bus. He was sporting a Bill Haley haircut, complete with a 'kiss-curl' and loads of Brylcream. He puffed on a John Player Navy Cut fag. Dave thought he looked familiar and, sure enough, there standing on the side of the road was the bold Mick Noonan junior, his brother.

He turned around, saw his brother and said, "Hi Dave," in an accent that Dave suspected had a slight English tone.

"Ah Jaysus! It's you Mick, it's great to see you, how is things?"

The two men walked together and soon, they arrived at the 'home place'. Mick stopped outside his beloved birthplace and all the memories of his happy childhood came flooding back. He had missed home so much.

Kate and Pat were delighted and surprised to see their 'prodigal' son. Kate wanted to scold Mick for not coming at Easter and for not letting them know he was coming but she was so overjoyed to see him, all of that was forgotten. She hugged her 'child' tightly and kissed his handsome face. Pat wanted to kiss him but his was not a 'kissing' family and showing emotion was not encouraged. However, he did allow himself to give his son a gentle pat on the back. Later on, while father and son discussed this, that and the other, Pat asked his son where he went to Mass in London and what was his parish priest's name. Luckily, Mick remembered the local priest's name in time – or did he make it up?

Later, Mick went to the town with Dave for a drink in Pitts. He met many of his friends there and he was expected to buy them all a drink, as he was home from England and therefore had loads of cash. Some of his so-called friends resented Mick paying with

'English' money, which was readily taken over counters in bars and shops, as money was money. There was still that inbred hatred of anything British in Ireland but many made exceptions for cash. In reality, Mick didn't have that much but he had to pretend he did, as he had a reputation to keep up. The craic was mighty and, with the intake of plenty of Guinness, sprits were high. He saw the 'Congo' along the counter and remarked:

"How are ye Congo? I saw you when you had nothing and you still have fuck all."

Congo took it well and all roared with laughter. After all, he got a couple of free pints from the returned exile.

Show Time

August brought the excitement of the carnival to town. It arrived for the late bank holiday weekend and beyond, and was the highlight of the summer season for the young Noonans. The large trucks appeared, trundling down Main Street with disassembled merry-go-rounds and rides of all kinds loaded in the trailers. Big bold letters and beautiful decorations on the sides of the vehicles told all that the carnival was coming to town. It would open on Friday night and remain in the town until Sunday week. There were two whole weekends to enjoy and the fun fair was even open in the evenings during the week.

The weather was very good on Friday and at last, after tea, the children headed to town on their bikes. They passed many others on their way and great excitement filled the air. The music of the organ could be heard in the distance and soon, they arrived at the parish field, parked the bikes and joined the crowd milling around.

Sean quickly joined the queue for the chair planes and waited with great anticipation for his much loved ride. He fastened the chain across the chair and, when all the seats were filled, the great tower began to rotate. As the pace picked up, the chairs flew outwards and upwards, giving a brilliant feeling of flying through the air to all the passengers. The boys and girls cheered and howled with joy and, as the rotation of the tower reached its peak, Sean looked down at the crowds and enjoyed every minute of the thrilling ride.

Sean was delighted to meet his best friend, Seamus as he made his way to his next favourite ride, the swinging boats, as the minimum 'crew' was two. The two boys climbed on board a middle boat and the attendant handed them the ropes. Soon, they were pulling hard on the ropes and each pull made the boat climb higher and higher. They were competing with Andy and Peader, in the nearby boat, to see who would get the highest. As they got higher and higher, they felt the brake being applied by the attendant pushing a board against the bottom of their boat. Sadly, the ride was coming to an end and the competition would have to continue another time.

The children tried as many rides as their pocket money would allow, which included a ride on the bumper cars and the hobbyhorses. The bumper cars were great fun; you could give a lad you didn't like much a good whack up the rear. This was, of course, against the rules but, when the place was full, the attendant couldn't see everything. Some boys deliberately bashed into a car with girls in it, to give them a good scare. The children also played 'push halfpenny' and other games, which were really stacked against them but, even so, they all enjoyed their evening at the carnival.

More excitement came to the town in late September, in the form of Tom Duffy's circus. Again, Sean and his siblings really looked forward to it. At last, the big weekend came and the big trucks came trundling through the town. The elephant trumpeted from inside his trailer and the horses kicked their stalls in their nervous excitement. The trucks and trailers were painted in bright colours, all adding to the fun of the fair. As the 'parade' passed along Main Street, two clowns jumped from a jeep towing a caravan and danced around, bashing each other with brooms and frying pans. The crowd loved it. The children cheered and clapped and everyone looked forward to a fun weekend.

Sean, Peader, Andy and Rose had tickets for the Saturday matinée and counted down the hours to the show. They became a bit worried when, in the morning, dark clouds gathered and then, to their disappointment, the rain came down very heavily. Despite this, they made their way to the town wearing raincoats, hats and wellies.

They arrived at Murphy's large garden, where the circus men had erected the big top the day before. People were going in but the ground was becoming muddier and muddier. Straw was laid down to soak up the water and the mud. The children were glad they wore their wellingtons. Soon they were seated, ready for the fun to start.

The ringmaster, wearing a red coat and top hat and sporting a black waxed moustache, announced the acts. The crowd roared with laughter when the clowns appeared, sliding and slipping in the muddy ring, bashing each other and making fools of themselves. They invited the children to join in the banter and fun. Sean enjoyed the trapeze artists' display of their amazing skills and fitness. He loved the elephants as they obeyed their trainer and dutifully trundled around the ring. A brave lion tamer put his head into the beast's mouth, which scared many of the audience and the local girls could not help but fall in love with the handsome Italian performer. Beautiful girls rode out on well-groomed white ponies with white plumes waving above their heads. The lovely, shapely girls did their best not to look too cold in their skimpy outfits and smiled broadly but some failed and just gritted their teeth.

Everyone had a wonderful afternoon despite getting wet, even in the big top which leaked in many places and the Noonan family made their way home, discussing each act, arguing about which was the best.

School Days

The Forty Hours took place in the church in October. It began on Sunday with a High Mass. The boys' choir took part in the three days of services. High Mass lasted well over an hour, with most of the prayers sung, either by the choir or by the priest and the student priests from the seminary. Both the priest and the choir sang prayers such as the *Gloria* and the *Credo*. Incense was used extensively and rituals acted out to the full. Sean was a choir member, which he enjoyed, even if the Latin words made little sense to him. Monday and Tuesday mornings had High Masses also and it was customary for the boys to get off early from school those days. This was an added attraction for all the boys.

"O'Hagen, come to the board and do that sum you failed to do for your homework. You brat!" the Rab roared.

It was the Tuesday after the High Mass and the boys' hopes were dashed when the Headmaster announced, as they filed into the classroom, "Don't think you brats are going home early today because you are not."

Doom and gloom descended on the students and it was back to work as usual.

John O'Hagen was not the sharpest knife in the drawer and he usually 'cogged' his homework from one of his classmates. He expected to get home early because of the Forty Hours and hadn't bothered doing any homework. The Rab pounced on him on return from the church and demanded to see his work. Of course none was done.

John stood at the blackboard, hands shaking, trying desperately not to drop the chalk. He copied out the mathematical problem from his tattered homework book as best he could and then proceeded to solve it. His first attempt was hopelessly incorrect and he received a slap on the ear from the Rab.

"Do it again, you braaat," he shouted, and John dropped the chalk.

"Pick it up," he roared and hit the boy again.

John's ears rang and he found it difficult to concentrate. He got the answer wrong again and received yet another head slap. This performance went on for several minutes, which seemed a lifetime to John and the Headmaster gradually lost control. His face reddened and he proceeded to whack the unfortunate student with the cane across his back. John's glasses flew off and the remnants of a watch he was wearing scattered on the floor, having been hit by the stick in the frenzy. Finally, the Rab relented and ordered John to his seat, asking one of his 'pets' (nicknamed 'Perfume' because of the talcum powder he usually wore) to complete the sum. 'Perfume' was the son of a well-off local shop owner. He rarely, if ever, got the cane.

The Rab settled behind his desk and composed himself. The boys eyed him from lowered heads, wondering what he was going to do next. Then, he took one of his coughing fits and his face began to turn a deep purple while he mopped his bald head with his white handkerchief.

"Noonan, get the Famel Syrup immediately and what are you all staring at? Get back to your books you brats." His mood was definitely going downhill and the pupils were very worried indeed.

Sean went to the teacher's room for the bottle of cough mixture, still hearing the Headmaster coughing his guts out. He delayed as long as he could but the Rab screamed, "Noonan, where are you?"

Sean delivered the Famel Syrup and soon, the patient's coughing eased and with that, the church bells began to toll out the

Angelus. Up stood the teacher and the boys and they began the prayers in Irish. Only the older boys knew the words; the rest mimed or blurted out their own version. Luckily, the Rab was not listening, as his cough had not ceased completely.

A few weeks before the Forty Hours, a lot of classroom time was devoted to practising the hymns. The Rab was once a sought-after tenor and he had sung at many weddings. This, he had to give up due to his coughing fits. The singing classes were conducted, as ever, with the threat of the cane hanging over those who did not sing to his satisfaction. Several canings were administered, with even a few whacks across the ears. The singing practice would begin with the Headmaster singing out:

"Chanadh dooooooe." – 'sing doe' in Irish however, the boys heard "*Nooooooe*" and the response would be ...

"Chanadh dooooe not nooooe, you braaats."

Andy Noonan was perceived by the Rab to be not singing loud enough and he shouted at him to open his mouth. Andy tried but failed miserably, he received a whack on the ear and the teacher shoved a ruler in his mouth sideways.

When the Rab meted out punishment, he remembered how each boy reacted. Those of a very nervous disposition had the tips of their fingers held, to ensure the hand was not withdrawn at the last second, thus wasting precious energy. In extreme cases, those who were receiving cranial punishment had their toes stepped on, to prevent swift backward movement, again wasting energy. Some boys squealed loudly, others merely whimpered and some stared the 'torturer' in the face in an act of defiance. Those that refused to cry were often given additional slaps, as it annoyed the Headmaster considerably.

One morning, a truck carrying crates of Coca Cola almost overturned, due to the driver underestimating the sharp bend at the end of Main Street, shedding much of its load onto the road and pavement. It happened at about 8.45am when the children were on their way to school. A crowd soon gathered at the scene. The driver was a bit shaken up but luckily, the falling cargo and the resultant broken glass injured no one. However, many of the bottles remained intact. The bright boys loaded these into their school bags and pockets and headed for school. Much trading went on in the school and money was made. Unfortunately for the boys, the Rab received a message that his pupils had indulged in thievery and he ordered all school bags to be opened for examination. The Coca Cola bottles were removed and the bag owners were lined up. Six slaps each were administered, following a lecture on the Seventh Commandment.

The boys settled down at their desks after much shuffling around, storing school bags underneath their desks. Mr Wallace roared out, "Quiet Pleeese! Roll call."

"Sean O'Noonawn."

"Anseo" (*here*).

"Meehall O'Bradigh."

"Anseo."

"Pairic de Burca."

"*Pairic de Burca????*"

"Nil se anseo," (*he is not here*) the boys replied in unison.

The roll call continued. Most of the boys were present but there were some suspicious absences, including one Patrick Burke (Padhraic de Burca). All names were called in Irish. If the teacher wasn't sure of a pupil's name in the mother tongue, he invented one beginning with an 'O' or 'Mac'.

Sean was sometimes given the task of cycling to an absent boy's address, to report on why he had not shown up at school. He was only too pleased to get out of the classroom but didn't always relish meeting the culprit. At times, the weather was not the best for cycling either. He could be bullied into telling the Headmaster a complete lie like, "His mother told me he was sick and in bed."

Often he would opt for, "I got no answer, Sir!" or, "I wasn't sure which was house was his, Sir!" If Sean told the truth and said that the absentee was 'mitching' and he saw him hiding behind a wall near the Puck's bridge, he would perhaps receive a beating from the same culprit at a later date.

Pupils who 'mitched' from school faced difficult decisions – e.g. how long would they 'mitch' for and how long could they keep up the pretence from their parents? Word would get around that a boy was not at school. The boy himself could get bored or get wet when spending many hours in a ditch, or under a hedge in a lonely field with only cows and sheep for company. There was also the problem of timing. He had to calculate at what time he should venture home. If he was lucky he would see some boys heading home and simply join them. If he got his calculations wrong, or if he thought he missed seeing the boys heading home, he might go home too early to face obvious consequences. Either way, the 'mitcher' would, sooner or later, have to face going back to school and the notorious Rab.

"Burke, where were you yesterday?"

"I wasn't very well, Sir!"

"Not very well, what was the matter?"

"I had a pain in my stomach, Sir."

"Is it better now?"

"Yes, Sir."

"Where is the note from your mother?"

"I lost it, Sir."

"How did you lose it Burke?"

"It slipped through the hole in me pocket, Sir."

"You little liar, hold out your hand!"

"But Sir, I was sick Sir, I was sick Sir, I really was Sir!"

Whack, whack, whack.

Sad News

On 22 November 1963, Sean and his family settled down to watch television after tea. He had finished his homework and looked forward to a comfortable evening of family viewing but then, there was a sudden halt to the programme and a solemn announcer's voice imparted the shocking news that President John F Kennedy had been shot in Dallas and had, sadly, died. The family was stunned, as was the whole of Ireland and the world. There was disbelief, shock, horror, sorrow and, finally, grief. How could this have happened to a man who was in Ireland only five months before? The family stared at the television, hoping it was all a hoax: but it was not. The great man was dead. The joy of his visit, so short a time ago, had turned to sorrow and despair. How could the world continue after such an evil event?

Soon, Ireland would watch, as did the rest of the world, the tragic pictures of Jackie Kennedy, still wearing her bloodstained suit, coming from the hospital and Lyndon B Johnson being sworn in as the new President, on board Air Force One. Éamonn de Valera made a broadcast on Radio Éireann that evening, in which he said:

> *"You will all have heard of the tragic death of President Kennedy. I am here, simply to give public expression to our common sorrow. We sympathise with all the people of the United States but in particular, with his grief-stricken wife and other members of his family. During his recent visit here, we came to regard the President as one of ourselves, though always aware that he was the head of the greatest nation in the world today. We were proud of him as being of our race and we were convinced that, through his*

*fearless leadership, the United States would continue
increasing its stature amongst the nations of the world and
its power of maintaining world peace. Our consolation is
that he died in a noble cause and we pray that God will
give to the United States another such leader."*

Most of Ireland watched the very sad funeral in Washington on TV
and the doom and gloom continued for months after that terrible
assassination.

Things to Come

Nineteen-sixty-four was to be a big year for the Noonan family. Pat and Kate's son, Tom, was in his final year and would be ordained in December at Dalgan Park. They had looked forward so much, all these years, for their son to say Mass for them. What joy there would be for the whole extended family! There was always the thought at the back of their mind that Tom would have to leave them for seven years and go to a foreign land. They preferred not to think about this but to look forward to the Ordination itself. Who would have to be invited? Who could they leave out? There were only limited places for the service.

Tom was ordained a Deacon the year before Ordination. The curriculum they followed was the same as that taught in the seminary in Maynooth. The Catholic Church, was after all, a 'Universal' church, so no deviations were acceptable.

Tom did not learn, until just before the Ordination, that he would be assigned to the Philippines. He would receive little information about the country he was about to work in. He would have to find out for himself about the vastly different culture there, the politics, the language problems due to dozens of different dialects and so on. He would have to contend with homesickness and loneliness. There would also be the Asian diet to deal with, which did not always agree with Western folk. Some missionaries would never be able to adjust to it.

The Philippines also had a tremendous difference in climate towards what he was used to in Ireland. There, he would have to endure extreme temperatures of 100 degree Fahrenheit and then, there would be the typhoons and the long rainy season. Even the danger of volcanic action was possible in that country. Then there were the Americans, who loved to drink in the many bars and avail of the prostitutes who readily accepted their dollars.

All this was ahead of him but, for now, the focus was on the Ordination in December. However, Tom knew there would be tremendous challenges and he relished and looked forward to them. He was eager to be a priest, at last and anxious to be out in the missionary field, doing the work he would be ordained for.

Sean also looked forward to the big day. He once thought about going for the priesthood himself but, at the age of fourteen, his thoughts in that direction were starting to wane and he was beginning to notice the opposite sex a bit more. He went to a 'boys-only' school, so direct contact with girls didn't happen there. He met girls in the town and at football matches and he liked them. However, he was a bit shy and didn't chat them up like his friends did.

In the summer, his neighbour, Josie Farrell's nephew, Conor O'Dwyer, came on holiday from Manchester. He was younger than Sean but was very street wise. He could chat up the girls without any problem and they loved it. He was trying to explain to Sean the simple facts of life.

Sean knew the way animals copulated but he had difficulty relating the same act to humans, especially his parents. Cattle, dogs and cats did it from behind and he found relating this to humans a problem. Anyway, he was sure the male enjoyed it but didn't think the female was too happy about it. This, he assumed from watching the fowl. When the cock stood on the hen's back and gripped her neck with his beak, the hen did not appear to enjoy it and the cock only spent a short time in the act. He therefore had the idea that sex was a 'male' thing.

Sean wondered how he would tell a sexual sin in Confession if he did it with a girl. He heard about 'adultery' as in, "Thou shalt not commit adultery" but he thought one had to be married to commit that sin. So, he was very confused about the whole thing. Conor O'Dwyer told him once that a Chinese girl had a horizontal fanny but poor Sean did not even know what the orientation of an Irish girl's vagina was (not that he was familiar with the word 'vagina' either). He had heard the 'C' word used extensively, which he knew referred to the female genitals but the word had many uses in everyday life. It was used as a noun, an adjective etc. It was not as versatile as the 'F' word but it was handy in colloquial conversation.

At this time, The Beatles were on the scene and the song *Help!* was getting a lot of air play. "Help, you know I need someone" were some of the words and Sean was taking notice of this concept. He felt he needed a girlfriend, or even girlfriends and he was moving away from the company of boys. Girls were, indeed, lovely creatures but how could he get to know one? This was the problem. Conor O'Dwyer could be laughing with a girl one minute and the next, be kissing her. What was the secret?

Ordination

Tom came home for his holidays in June. Everyone was pleased to see him. He was wearing a round collar as he was now a deacon and people saluted him in the street. How proud his dear parents were! Sean and his brothers went with him to Croke Park in Dublin, to see a football match and Sean was amazed when people doffed their hats and saluted him in O'Connell Street.

Tom still insisted that he worked on the farm at Burtons but he was given very light duties in the beginning. The farm workers did not know how to respond to him but Tom just asked them to treat him as one of themselves. They did their best but cursing and swearing became much less prevalent: sometimes, however, the lads forgot themselves and it all came out.

Paddy Kennedy was never a man to do too much work and liked to chat to his workmates when the chance arose. Jim Burke was the charge hand and liked to please the boss. He told Paddy off several times for slacking but Paddy had a cunning plan. When making hay, the old Ferguson tractor would bring in loads of hay on the buck-rake and dump it where the cock was being constructed. When Paddy needed a break, he slyly turned off the fuel tap at the side of the engine, the tractor continued for a few minutes and then began to splutter and eventually the engine died. Billy, the driver, hopped off and started to check all the known causes. Was the machine out of fuel? Did a belt snap? In the meantime, Paddy was enjoying a well-deserved rest, until Billy copped the 'adjusted' fuel tap and jumped about with rage. He knew who the culprit was but couldn't prove it.

Tom resumed his studies at Dalgan Park in September and his Ordination day was set for Saturday, 20 December 1964. The preparations were made. His sister, Mary, was given the task of making his vestments: her employer was delighted to let her do it at her shop. Kate Noonan was busy making a list of who would be invited to the Ordination itself, which included a reception afterwards and to a celebration lunch following his first Mass in the church in his native town on Sunday 21st. There was great excitement in the Noonan household. Mick came home from England for the event and for Christmas. He sported his usual up-to-date fashion outfit. He even had a tattoo emblazoned on his arm. His parents were not too impressed with it, even though it was inscribed 'Mum and Dad' and 'love you always'. The local girls loved him to dance with him and they all wanted to be his steady girlfriend. Mick relished every minute of it.

The week before Ordination, the bishop of Meath came to talk to the candidates about the ceremony and about their chosen vocation. He went through the proceedings that would take place on Saturday morning. He spoke about the challenges that they would face, especially in the first five years as a priest. It would not be easy at times and he went on to say that some of them would leave the priesthood, to follow other careers and others would leave to get married. Tom and his classmates felt somewhat like being at the Last Supper, when Christ said that one of them would betray him. Like the Apostles, they all said that they would never leave their Master and would remain faithful to Him, even unto death. However, several of the students wondered about the life they were embarking on. That Friday night, one of them silently left the seminary and never returned. One of his thoughts was what God said to Adam in Genesis, "It is not good for man to be alone." His family were so disappointed and embarrassed when they learnt the news on Saturday morning.

The morning was cold, with some frost but sunny and the low sun shone through the bare trees that surrounded Dalgan Park, making the grass sparkle. The Noonan family arrived early and found their way to the church, which was quickly filling up. There was great excitement. The women wore their best outfits, some chosen and purchased especially for the great occasion. Kate and Pat were so proud of their son when the bishop conferred Holy Orders on him. Their dream had come true. Everything went very well and everyone was pleased. After the service, Tom's parents and all the family took their turn and knelt in front of him to receive his first blessing. His parents were moved to tears of sheer joy. What a great day it was!

The family and their friends enjoyed a reception for Father Tom that afternoon, in a local hotel. Everyone enjoyed it, especially the family and the extended family. They also looked forward to his first Mass the next day. Tom was certain that he wanted to receive the sacrament of Holy Orders, with its vows of poverty, chastity and obedience and he was determined to be a priest forever. He looked forward to his life on the missions and the challenges that lay ahead.

However, between 1969 and 1977, one hundred and seventy-seven men would leave the Society of the Columban Fathers and the priesthood.[2] Thousands of men left the priesthood worldwide in the years following the second Vatican Council. Many would feel that Vatican II had let them down when the bishops voted to retain the celibacy rule. They could not continue as single and lonely men. Others would leave for different reasons, such as being disillusioned by life on the missions and thinking that it was not the life for them. Some would believe that their superiors had let them down. Some would come to depend on alcohol and other substances, and not be able to continue in that life. Nevertheless, many priests remained faithful to their vocation and embraced the life. The future years would see more mature men coming forward for Ordination and fewer boys coming straight from

---

[2] *Fat God, Thin God* by James Kennedy. Mercier Press, 2002

school. They would have experienced life as a layperson and, only then, they would decide on a religious life.

Fifty years later, Sean Noonan visited Dalgan Park. He was pleased to see that the building was very busy. Missionary work had changed completely. Yes, the older generation of ordained men were there, on retirement and also on holiday but a younger generation was now taking different paths in bringing relief to the Third World and helping those in need. They encouraged the development of new eco-systems in trying to sustain the earth. Christianity was still central to their cause but now, fewer men were being ordained, especially in Ireland. The 'foreign' lands of old were now producing their own priests and developing the Church in their native lands. Things had certainly changed.

Sean revisited the beautiful church where Tom had been ordained all those years before. There, in the side aisle, sat an old missionary priest in his wheelchair, eyes closed, completely at one with his Friend and Master present there on the altar, which he had served for over sixty years. He remained faithful to Jesus and his life was very happy indeed. Yes, there were ups and downs but he had persevered. He gave thanks to the Lord as he meditated on his spiritual life and experiences, and looked forward to meeting his Master when his life on earth would end: "It is in dying that we are born to eternal life" – St Francis of Assisi.

The Band

In the New Year of 1966, Sean decided to join the local brass and reed band in the town. His older brother, Dave, was already a member and Mick had been one before he went to England. His mother was not keen on the idea. Kate said that it led to drinking and Sean would be only sixteen later in that year. She was right of course but Sean dismissed it and thought only of the music and the 'glory' of marching down the town, and even in Dublin City. That year would see the fiftieth anniversary of the Easter Rising. There was going to be a big parade in Dublin on Saint Patrick's Day and Sean hoped that he would be ready to march with the rest of the band. He was certainly going to give it his best shot.

He joined one dark, cold January evening and was delighted to see some of his friends and classmates joining too. There was Andy Green and the 'Balla' Flanagan already there and ready to start music lessons. The bandmaster, Mr Timmons, began by introducing the boys to music and how it is written. It seemed like Chinese writing to Sean and he found it quite a challenge. The benches the students sat on were old church pews, as the band hall was once the village Catholic Church. He tried his best to concentrate and, when he faltered and had a giggle at a gesture the Balla had made, one of the older band stalwarts, Bartle O'Grady, shouted out, "Hey young Noonan, where do you think you are, at a fuken weddin'?"

Sean persevered and soon, he was learning to play the 'cornet'. It was shorter than a trumpet with three valves, which were operated by the right hand. The left hand held the instrument to the mouth and the lip had to be pursed in the right fashion, in order to make the sound. This was quite difficult and could result in a disfigured lip if one played too much. Even professional trumpet and cornet players suffered from this. In the beginning, one's "lip could go" and when this happened, one could not play anymore.

The instruments were very old and they were made by a famous firm called *Boosey and Hawks*. The Duke of Leinster had donated them in the nineteenth century. The good Duke had lived only a few miles from the town, albeit in a Palladian mansion and he was a big patron of the area.

Employment and trade depended on the big estates from the Seventeenth to the early Twentieth century but, following the decline and fall of the dukes, they were all but forgotten. The new Irish Republic did not recognise British titles etc. and the many landlords, with their big houses and walled demesnes, simply ran out of money. Their land was compulsorily purchased by the Land Commission. Some landlords took advantage of the offers they received under the Wyndham Act of 1903 and many returned to Britain and others sold their estates, to live more modestly. Strangely, the fact that the Duke of Leinster once lived in the local town land was never mentioned in the national school. Perhaps the teachers themselves didn't realise the fact or were not really interested. After all, such titles were throwbacks from British Imperialism in Ireland.

The old instruments tasted of bad brass and left a peculiar taste in the mouth. The band room was quite cold but a pot-bellied stove in the centre threw out great heat and became red hot; one's back could be quite cold however.

Sean was slow in reading music and getting the hang of the cornet and he became worried about the big parade. He envied 'Gandhi' Dillon, who was the bass drum player and could also 'play' the triangle. All he had to do was keep time, which he did not always manage, while Sean struggled with the notes and translating them to his instrument. However, he was delighted when Mr Timmons and Bartle O'Grady agreed to let him march with the band on Saint Patrick's Day and to mime playing the cornet.

At last, the big day came and Sean cycled into the town, proudly wearing his band uniform. The uniform was an old 'Garda' issue in navy blue, brass buttons with a white covered cap. The cloth was rough and the trousers itched and irritated his leg. Another problem was that the waist came to just below his nipples. He wore braces to hold them up and then, the cloth irritated his skin, especially the legs and around the 'private' area. No way was he going to remove the jacket, which would reveal his embarrassment. Anyway, Sean decided it was worth the sacrifice to have the honour of marching in Dublin, on that memorable and auspicious day.

The band first marched up Main Street after Mass and the crowds cheered as they passed by. Then, they boarded a coach for their journey to Dublin. They assembled on York Street. The fifteen men were full of anticipation. It was not the largest band in the parade, but it was the proudest. Sean relished the occasion and the best part was passing the General Post office in O'Connell Street, where the historic Rising began and where all the dignitaries, including Éamonn de Valera, were now assembled. Sean felt very proud indeed. He would remember this day forever. RTÉ had shown a series of programmes on television, in which the events of Easter 1916 were re-enacted as if they had been actually filmed at the time. It was very interesting indeed. Many foreign TV stations broadcast the series.

The coach brought them back to the town and they deposited their instruments in the band hall. Then the big decision came for Sean. Most of the men were going for a drink in Pitt's public house; would he join them? He decided to go along as his brother, Dave, was going as well. Would he have a drink or would he not? That was his second big decision. In the end he chanced a bottle of Smithwicks ale. At first it was not too bad but then it began to taste too bitter. His mother's words came back to him: "Sean, never drink or never smoke."

He did have a little smoke as well. His mother hid her 'butts' behind the old clock on the mantel piece, to be retrieved later. He would pinch one and a few matches and light up in the shed. The first few drags caused him to cough and splutter but, as all his school pals smoked, he decided to persevere and be one of the boys. He felt sick after smoking the butt yet, he foolishly wanted to be as the others boys were and continued to acquire the habit. Later on, when he did the messages on Saturday morning, his bought ten Carrolls with the tips he had received or, if the tips were not up to it, he would buy two or three loose fags. If the tips were really good, he could afford to buy ten Major. He could really be one of the boys with ten Major, as they were the 'class' cigarettes of the time. Some of the older boys smoked English cigarettes, such as Benson and Hedges or Piccadilly and even the luxury brand of Rothmans.

Sean played with the band the whole summer, at matches and fête and they even entered a brass and reed band competition in Dún Laoghaire, where they came last (of five bands). However, it was a great experience for him and all the musicians. When Christmas came, the band played carols around the town. It was cold but enjoyable. When they visited the convent, all the nuns came to the door. They really enjoyed the music and sang along. When they finished, the nuns chatted with the men, asked who they were and told them that they educated their brother or sister or even their mother.

Tragedy

In September, the Noonan family got a letter from Tom in the Philippines. He was now nearly a year away from home and he told about his time learning the language in Manila. He found the strange language, Filipino, quite difficult but English was widely spoken, which was a help.

He had made good friends in the college. He went to the cinema at weekends and had a few games of golf with his many new acquaintances and friends. He helped with saying Mass in the city on Sundays. It was great experience and he looked forward to joining a parish soon and to trying out the language on the locals. He was not sure which parish he would be going to and he hoped he would be working with an amiable parish priest.

The weather was difficult with extreme heat and humidity. The rainy season was something else. He wrote about his wonderful trip out to the Philippines: flying to New York, staying a few days there, seeing the Statue of Liberty, Central Park and many other exciting areas. Then he mentioned the flight to San Francisco and having another enjoyable rest in that beautiful city. Tom loved seeing the Golden Gate Bridge and venturing over it, to the vineyards beyond in Napa Valley. His most memorable experience was staying over in Hawaii, enjoying the beautiful scenery and weather there.

His first impressions of Manila were mixed. The population was obviously great and the city had a distinct Asian atmosphere. He was not really prepared for it and he did not know what, for sure, to expect. However, he soon settled in with fellow priests, mostly from Ireland and the home sickness wasn't so bad.

Sean remembered the day that Tom went away and how devastated the whole family had been, especially his dear parents. His father had gone to his room; when he returned his eyes were very red and his breath smelt of whiskey. Mother just cried and cried. This was the price they had to pay to see their son a priest. They knew this day would come but they always hid their thoughts and fears away, in the back of their minds. Dave drove Tom to the airport with Mary: it would have been too much for Pat and Kate. Mary and Dave also felt very sad when they bid him goodbye at the terminal at Dublin Airport. Tom put on a very brave face but when they were gone, he had a little weep himself. He prayed hard for the strength to bear this cross and turned his mind to the adventures that lay ahead.

As Sean finished reading Tom's letter, he noticed a telegram boy parking his bike at the gate and heading towards the door. The telegram was addressed to Patrick and Kathleen Noonan. He thanked the boy, gave him a sixpence and brought the sealed message to his mother and father. They froze with fear, as telegrams seldom brought good news. Pat opened it with trembling hands and had to sit down when he read it.

"Pat, Pat what is it? What does it say?" cried Kate already welling up.

The telegram read:

> *Deep regret stop your son Michael Noonan stop has*
> *passed away as a result of an industrial accident stop*

Kate fainted. Sean just managed to catch her and sat her down on a chair. Pat buried his face in his hands, in floods of tears.

Mick had been given an offer of a job extending the relatively new M1 Motorway in the North London area, south of Elstree. The work was hard but Mick preferred it to work in the city. The ganger picked him up at six in the morning. The day was long but the craic was great. The money was generous and he knew many of the lads. He drove a JCB digger, removing soil for the motorway extension. Whilst driving the mechanical digger, Mick came to a narrow stretch of the site and the soil at the edge collapsed, due to recent rain. The heavy machine began to slide sideways and overturned into the ravine, throwing him from his seat and crushing him underneath. His colleagues saw it happen and rushed to the scene. When eventually he was removed from under the machine, he was already dead.

Mick had just returned to England from a two-week holiday to his home place. He spent his time visiting his many friends and going to the dances in the town. He helped his father with bringing in the hay and had the craic with his brothers and sisters. It was a magical time for all and when he left, he promised to see them all at Christmas. His parents were, naturally, very sad to see him go and looked forward to seeing him again in a few months. Little did they know, they would never see him alive again!

His body was brought back from England a few days later. The coffin was accompanied by his personal effects in a small suitcase. The family was numb with grief. Tom wanted to come home but there was no time. The wake was held in his home place. Sean gazed at his dead brother in the coffin, wearing a brown habit that hid his crushed chest. A rosary was intertwined like teardrops through his fingers. A holy picture of Jesus and Mary was placed on his chest. There was not a grey hair on his head; so young, so lively only a few weeks before, now so still in that eternal box.

The neighbours came throughout the day to pay their respects, including the 'deaf and dumb' man, Pat Brady. When the evening came, the coffin was closed after the Rosary and other prayers were said. The very sad removal to the chapel took place. Pat and Kate were beside themselves with sorrow; how could God allow their son to be taken from them like this? Did they deserve this? The bell of the chapel tolled loudly and sadly as the coffin was carried in. The church was filled with friends and neighbours and townsfolk who wished to offer their condolences.

The funeral was equally sad. Someone placed the jersey of the local football team on the coffin, which was soon covered in flowers. Some of the family walked behind the hearse to the cemetery and the brass and reed band marched in front. The Rosary was recited as the coffin was lowered into the deep, cold and silent grave and a lone cornet player from the band played the *Last Post*. The sods were shovelled into the grave, making a hollow thud on the coffin lid. Sean felt empty and his sadness was the worst he had ever experienced. It was difficult to see how life would go on without his brother, Mick, being around.

Growing Up

Christmas 1966 was difficult but the family did their best not to let their grief overcome them. Mick would not have wanted them to be sad. It was especially hard for his parents but they got through it.

January was bright and cold. Sean was nearly seventeen and was allowed to go to a dance in the town with his brother, Dave. The dance hall stood on the corner of Main Street. A local man, who had won fifty thousand pound in the Irish Sweepstake, had built it. It was a massive amount of money at the time and his family wanted him to invest his money, instead of spending it all in the pub. He spent a lot of it in the pub anyway but, at least he provided somewhere for parishioners to enjoy themselves.

Sean gave himself a good wash and had a shave. His beard started to appear when he was about sixteen and he was a little embarrassed about it. He decided, one evening, to shave it off and used his father's Gillette razor, which was in the washstand drawer. He placed a blade into the device and tightened it up. He was nervous but felt he had to shave. He managed it quite well but nicked himself in several places. He stemmed the blood with small pieces of toilet paper. His mother and sisters burst out laughing when he appeared, dotted with pieces of paper. However, he had received his own razor from his sister, Mary, at Christmas.

Having now shaved without any nicks, Sean applied the obligatory dollop of Brylcream hair oil and matted it down. He borrowed some Old Spice aftershave he found in the cupboard. He checked himself in the mirror and thought, 'Are you ready for some dancing, you handsome brute?'

He arrived at the parish hall, where dances took place on Friday and Saturday nights. He was very excited and a little nervous when he paid his six shillings and entered the hall. The band was setting up on the stage and boys and girls were moving around, eyeing up each other. Some couples found seats and chatted to each other. They bought 'minerals': Seven Up, orange, red lemonade and Coca Cola, in the 'non-alcoholic' bar. Tayto Crisps and Jacobs's biscuits were also available. Sean bought himself and Dave some crisps and a lemonade each. Dave would have preferred a creamy pint of Guinness.

The band started up with a rock and roll number. The punters were reluctant to be the first on the floor. Three girls ventured out and danced the 'twist'. Soon, others made their way out on the floor. Dave saw a girl he fancied and told Sean that he was going to ask her to dance. He suggested that he ask someone as well. Sean was desperately shy and did not know what to do. He followed Dave to where all the girls were congregating. Soon, most of the lads were heading for the same area.

Sean asked one girl; she refused but, to Sean's delight, another girl, beside her, said that she would. He took her by the hand and they made their way back towards the floor. Boys pushed against them and he nearly lost her several times. At last, they were on the floor. Sean decided to do the 'twist' in front of her and she did the same. When the music stopped, he chanced putting his arm around her and she did likewise. He liked this. Too soon, the three dances were finished and the girl left to return to the 'girls' corner of the hall. He didn't say much to her as he couldn't think of what to say. He thought that she liked him and he liked her. He felt a bit like the dog that chased cars: if he caught one, he wouldn't know what to do with it.

The band played the Engelbert Humperdinck number, *Release Me* and Sean asked another girl to dance. This was a slow dance and the girl danced quite close. Yes! Sean was really beginning to enjoy dancing! Again, he was shy but the girl chatted to him and he didn't feel quite so bad. He wished he knew how to chat to them like his English friend, Conor O'Dwyer. He had a respect for women and he tried to ignore what his school friends were telling him: "If a girl gives you three dances then you will get the ride!"

But Sean, for now anyway, was content if he just had a kiss and a cuddle and not the full 'cur isteach'.

Later the 'drunks' arrived in the hall after the pubs closed much to Sean's annoyance. They began to hassle the girls as most would not dance with them. It looked like there could be trouble, but thankfully nothing happened.

However, the evening ended too soon and he and Dave headed home. There was still the rest of the weekend to enjoy.

On Monday morning, Sean headed off to school. Next year, he would have to sit the Leaving Certificate exams. After that, he would be free from studying and the corporal punishment dished out by Mr Wallace, 'affectionately' known as the Rab. Although Sean and his classmates were growing up, they were still subjected to the humiliation of the cane and the slap around the ear. The Rab was becoming unable to reach the ears of Sean Dalton, a classmate of Sean's. Instead he was now resorting to insulting the taller boys like Dalton, with phrases such as, "Dalton! Laziness, when did you ever offend me?" or "You big, ugly traithneen you."

Sean was developing into a fine young man. School was getting tougher. He joined the local youth club where he could have a dance and enjoy the craic with his friends. At weekends, he ventured into the pub with his friend, Andy Green. Andy was a great consumer of Guinness and Sean decided to try a pint. They went to the bar in the local 'hotel', which was no longer a hotel but it had a fine bar. There was a long bar and in the middle, there was a 'snug', for the ladies.

Although the snug was attached to the bar, it had its own little bar area and entrance. The 'windows' were opaque with stained glass, advertising a whiskey whose distillery had long been extinct. The woodwork was ornate. The 'ladies' of the town, usually wearing a coat and headscarf, entered the bar from a side door and slipped into the snug, where they would not normally be seen by the male punters, who enjoyed the freedom of the open bar. Women had not been allowed into the bar in years past and some of them still preferred to drink in anonymity. Others came to collect, perhaps a large bottle of Guinness for home consumption and others told the barman that the three-quart can of stout was to make a 'porter cake'. The barman was sometimes sceptical but suppressed a grin, which might be taken the wrong way and which could be greeted by a few choice words from the female customer, such as, "What do you mean you little fuken toe-rag."

The snug was frequented by a certain lady of 'easy virtue' who made a living providing certain services to the local, richer men. Most knew what she was about but did not dare to say anything. Several of the local 'business' men ignored her during the day but secretly paid her a visit, or arranged to meet her at secret locations, during the hours of darkness. It was believed that the sum of five pounds was exchanged for a 'major' service. She bought herself a new Volkswagen Beetle and rumour had it that it was paid for in five pound notes. This was the hypocrisy of the town, which the local doctor regarded as a town of 'squinting windows'.

At weekends, the pub had impromptu music sessions, provided by fine musicians such as the 'Gandhi' Dillon and the 'Balla' Flanagan. 'Darcy' Murphy also joined in with his accordion. The session came to be known as 'Curley's Ceili', after the popular barman who served a very fine pint of stout. The two musicians were pleased if they got a few bob for their efforts. They considered money not to be a problem however, the lack of it definitely was. Jimmy Brennan was once asked about a new accordion player who played at the 'Ceili' but his only critique was that, "He played the bollix out of it!"

Sean waited in anticipation for his first pint of the black stuff. At last, Curly placed it on the counter with a knowing grin on his face.

"Drink that up, young Noonan and I hope you are eighteen, otherwise I am in the shit."

"Oh yes I am Cur..., I mean Mr Murphy," he lied, convincingly!

"There's your change, ta ta!"

Sean watched as the glass blackened up to a creamy head. He picked it up and, with a "Good luck, Andy", sipped the pint. It tasted a little on the bitter side but his second mouthful was delicious.

"Oh, that's wonderful Andy; here's to many more."

They enjoyed the music, joined in the singsong and Sean ordered two more pints. The first one was going a little to his head and he felt a little light-headed. The second pint went down well and he felt over the moon. School was again in the morning and he went out, jumped on his bike and cycled home.

When, several weeks later, Sean chanced the third pint things were different. He felt quite full as he made his way to where his bike was parked. He had a little difficulty throwing his leg across it but, as he made his way towards home, in the dark, his ears began to sing a little and he had to put more effort into the peddling. At last, he arrived home. As he went in, he felt his face burn.

His parents were, luckily, watching television. He thought he would go straight to bed. His mother asked if he was all right; he said that he was. He undressed and got himself under the covers. His face burned and his stomach felt not quite so well. The ceiling started to sway, in fact, the room started to sway. He held on tight to the bed but it was moving too. Up he jumped, made his way through the sitting room and out into the yard. Up came the

Guinness and his dinner and anything else that was in his stomach. God, he felt so ill! What had he done?

His parents knew what was going on but they did not know how to tackle it. It was something they could never broach with their sons. Sean's father was not a pub goer. It upset him to see his sons going there and bringing the family into disrepute but he did not know how to handle it. He only hoped that this was a one-off and that Sean would have the sense to do the right thing.

Sadly, the sixties had a 'pub' culture and a young man was not 'one of the lads' if he didn't take a drink and have a smoke. Footballers were expected to go to the boozer after a match and 'drink their fill of porter', like the character in The Clancy Brothers' song of the day, *The Bould Thady Quill*. Of course, there were exceptions but boozing was part of the culture and few had the sense, or courage, to be moderate in that direction.

Summer Days

That summer, Sean asked for a job in the Post Office. He had sat his Intermediate Certificate exams the year before and did very well. His teachers were very pleased and advised him to continue to work hard for his Leaving Cert. Sean was determined to do this but his last year was full of distractions. He enjoyed going to dances and to the youth club. He was getting to know and like girls and he even had his eye on one. He met her at the youth club but he was still very shy and often, was stuck for things to say. However, she seemed to like him anyway.

One weekend, he went with friends to a motorcycle race in Dunboyne. The race took place in the town itself. There was great excitement and soon, the bikes were flying through the narrow streets and disappearing over the narrow railway bridge. The noise was often deafening but it all added to the fun of the festival. The crowd waited anxiously for the riders to appear again and pass swiftly on the next lap. The only safety barriers were bales of straw, strategically placed at dangerous corners. The boys never knew who was racing, or who was winning but it did not matter; it was great fun. Sean dreamed of being a top-class motorcyclist and imagined himself standing on the podium, receiving his World Champion trophy while being gazed upon by the lovely ladies. There were little such celebrations in Dunboyne but there were trophies to be won.

Anyway, the postmaster was looking for someone to work to cover his postmen, who were given holidays in July and August. Sean came from a good family and, he thought, he would be ideal for the job. For his part, Sean was delighted to earn some money during the summer months. He would give some to his mother and he would have money of his own to spend for the first time in his life. What things he could do with it, he thought. The world was his oyster! In fact, the money he got did not go that far but there is no harm in dreaming!

The first morning, Sean was to 'shadow' John Sheridan on his route. John cycled very slowly, waving to and chatting with all and sundry. He explained who lived where and what dogs to watch out for. He brought newspapers to some on his route and was generously rewarded with Christmas boxes. John told Sean not to let on to Dick, the postmaster, about the papers.

After a week with each of the four postmen, Sean did the routes himself. Postman Ned Waldron was indeed a character. He was an elderly gentleman and cycled as if he was competing in a slow bicycle race. He was even slower than John Sheridan was. If he had a postcard for a house on the edge of his route, he would not deliver it on its own but wait until there was another letter. This could take several days.

The school was on Ned's route and during term time, it was a relief to hear him come through the swing doors dividing the primary and secondary classes. Ned would knock on the door and Mr Wallace would pop out for a chat, beginning with a loud, "Good morning, Ned". It reminded Sean of a line from Shakespeare: "Good morrow, Ned".

Of course, the inevitable bedlam would ensue and then, the Rab would return and administer punishment to the boys who were unfortunate enough to have been spotted misbehaving, and some were included among the 'usual suspects'.

Sean enjoyed cycling along the country roads and lanes. Wildlife was abundant. The larks sang high over the fields; blackbirds flew noisily from the hedgerows; rabbits grazed in the fields, forever listening out and watching for danger. The sheep and cattle stood and stared from the same fields, happily chewing the cud before returning to grazing with the rabbits. Sean remembered the poem, *Leisure*, which went:

> *What is this life if, full of care,*
> *We have no time to stand and stare.*
> *No time to stand beneath the boughs*
> *And stare as long as sheep and cows.*

> – W.H. Davis

Life was good.

Then there were the wet days, which were less pleasant and a postman could get soaked very easily in a summer shower. The wet gear was very cumbersome and it was a chore putting on the leggings and waterproof cape and then, taking it all off again when the sun returned.

One day, the summer calmness was disturbed. Sean heard them first. He looked up to see a formation of World War I aeroplanes approaching from the south. They were heading for an airfield from which numerous Tiger Moths had flown some years before. It was very exciting as he watched them descend behind the far off trees. He heard later, that they were replica biplanes and triplanes, painted in German and British livery for the film, *The Blue Max* starring George Peppard.

During the following weeks, Sean and all the local boys and girls enjoyed watching the film being made. There were excellent dog fights, with planes descending on fire only to be seen climbing up again, just clearing the trees. A helicopter 'camera ship' followed closely, which appeared to be too close for comfort. There was one accident near Dublin Bay when two helicopters did collide, resulting in fatalities but otherwise, it was safe. The special effects were magnificent. Later, Sean did get a chance to see the film but some of the enjoyment was taken from it, as he could recognise some of the scenery.

Postmen did quite a few favours for the people on their route. They brought newspapers to some and ran 'messages' for others. At Christmas, they were rewarded with a drink at almost every house. Often, they would have to be driven home, with their bikes loaded in the boot and their remaining cards not delivered.

Micky Flynn handed Sean a note and asked, as a favour, if he wouldn't mind placing a bet for him. Mickey lived quite far from the town and he fancied a particular horse in an afternoon race in Fairyhouse. Sean entered the betting shop and handed the clerk the slip of paper. The girl looked at it and then looked at it again.

"What is the name of the horse?" she asked.

"I don't know, let me have a look."

Sean could not make out the writing either. They both looked through the lists of runners but neither was sure of the horse. Sean thought that it was not that important, as the horse would not win anyway, so he didn't place a bet.

Next morning, Mickey was waiting on the road, rubbing his hands in anticipation of receiving his winnings.

"Well, young Noonan, how much did I get?"

"I didn't put the money on Mickey, as Miss Mooney couldn't make out your writing."

"What! You didn't place my bet! That horse was ten to one and it won! Why the fuck did you not read the slip?"

"I couldn't make it out either. Sorry Mickey, there's your half-crown."

"Sorry Mickey! Sorry Mickey! You fuken eejit!"

The weeks passed with good days and bad days. Sean was delighted with the money. He went to the dances in the town at the weekends and sometimes, to other towns such as Naas, when the big showbands were there. Among his favourites were Dicky

Rock and the Miami Showband, Brendan Bowyer and the Royal Showband, and Doc Carroll and the Royal Blues. He went to the youth club on a Wednesday night and enjoyed a few pints with his friends. Thoughts of going back to school were far from his mind.

School Days End

Sean tried to study for his Leaving Certificate but it was not easy: his social life got in the way of his studies. He was at that stage as a teenager when confusion set in, together with strange feelings that he had never known as a boy. He was neither a man nor a boy and that worried him. His world was changing fast.

There was much in the news about protests and unrest in Northern Ireland. An Taoiseach, Jack Lynch, met the Northern Ireland Prime Minister, Captain Terence O'Neill for talks in January, in Dublin. This did not please either the Unionists or the Republicans. The Northern Ireland civil rights movement had been active for several years but now, things were coming to a head. It was felt, by certain observers, that the fiftieth anniversary of the Easter Rising, two years before, had worried the Unionists while Nationalists thought again about their rights to housing, jobs and fair elections (one man one vote) while some dreamed of a united Ireland. It was strange that Christian people on a small island could not live together. Father Christopher Fox MHM, a missionary priest for over sixty years, would later write that religion often 'hid the face of God'. Factions used it for their own, often evil, agenda. John Lennon later wrote that his ideal world would have no countries and no religion – "nothing to kill or die for". Perhaps he had a point.

In the New Year, Sean knuckled down and studied for the final exam that came in June. The exam was difficult enough but, when they were finished, Sean's school days came to a close. He thought he would never see the day and now it was here. He felt very strange, a bit like a prisoner who has just been released from a fourteen-year jail sentence; almost institutionalised! What was he going to do?

Late June, 1968, Sean sat on the comfortable armchair, which now replaced the old homemade one, beside the Rayburn cooker, which replaced the open fire. He gazed out through the door and viewed the lovely summer's day. His whole life lay before him. What was he going to do now? There had been no real career information given at school. Mr Wallace, the dear Rab, merely encouraged further education, with little or no pointers as to where to obtain it. Vocational careers were somewhat frowned upon by the Headmaster and not encouraged. Now, his whole life lay before him; not like before, when it was just the long summer eight-week holiday. He thought about what lay ahead. He was now on his own. He felt loneliness and yet, he felt excitement. The world was now his oyster – but how deep was the sea?

Postscript

Father Tom returned home after his six years' 'tour of duty' on the missions and had occasion to say Mass in a parish in Dublin City. He noticed, during the service, an old, frail man in a blue suit and wearing a red tie, in among the congregation. He then realised it was his old teacher, Thomas Francis Wallace, the dear Rab.

The Rab approached him afterwards and, in a way, he was pleased to meet the old man after many, many years. Tom was somewhat surprised when the Rab said that he thought he may have been 'too hard on the boys of the town'. Was he sorry for being a sadistic bastard and did he, perhaps, really get some sexual satisfaction from flogging young boys, as was believed by many of his past pupils? Or, did he now realise that he would soon meet his Maker and he feared the reserved place in hell, which John O'Hagen maintained was waiting for him? Who knows!